Angels

FROM THE MEADOW

James Stanhope-Brown

The pictures on the front and back cover are copies of paintings by the Manchester artist John R. McGuire.
All drawings in this book by H. E. Tidmarsh are circa 1894.

During 1996, Charter Street Ragged School will celebrate its connections with the 150th anniversary of Manchester's first ragged school established in Nelson Street, and now an integral part of the Manchester Ragged School Museum.

Down through the years, many people have visited or had associations with Angel Meadow's ragged school district, each of them drawn to this unique part of Manchester for the same reason — "to save sinners and to alleviate hardship and poverty." Some of those visitors to the Meadow included such celebrities as Earl Shaftesbury, General Gordon, Dr Barnardo and Winston Churchill.

The drama you are about to read is based on true events and the facts have been fictionalised to improve the overall quality of this story.

James Stanhope-Brown

James Stanhope-Brown was born at Longsight, Manchester in September 1934. At the age of 2 years he was orphaned and placed into care at Manchester's largest orphanage — The Styal Cottage Homes.

Thirteen years later and with a scholarship to a Manchester high school, James began a new chapter of his life at Levenshulme and then at Fairfield, Droylsden.

Nowadays, as a local historian, James pursues his interests in the more unusual aspects of Manchester and Cheshire memorabilia whilst devoting any spare time to the Manchester Ragged School Museum.

Other books written by James Stanhope-Brown include —

'Manchester to Styal via Swinton'
'A Styal of its Own'

Designed and printed by
Revell & George Limited, Cow Lane, Oldfield Road,
Manchester M5 4NB   Tel: 061-745 7771
Published by Christine Pothecary, Woodford, Northants
Tel: 0832 73 3111
© Copyright James Stanhope-Brown 1991

ISBN 0-9515652-1-4

**Ten per cent of any profits from the sale of this
book will be donated to the following charities:**

**Barnardos
National Childrens Home
NSPCC
Boys and Girls Welfare**

My sincere thanks are due to the following societies, without
whose kind help this story could not have been told.

Boys' and Girls' Welfare Society
Wood Street Mission
Charter Street Mission and Ragged School
Disabled Living Services (Manchester)
Liverpool Central Library
Manchester Central Library
Sharp Street Ragged School
The Globe and Toronto Star Newspapers, Canada
The Greenfield Recorder and Worcester Evening Gazette, Massachusetts
The Quarrier Homes, Scotland
The NSPCC
The National Childrens' Homes

and, to anyone else whose name has been overlooked.

A very special thanks is owed to Linda Batty of the
Northfield Mt. Hermon School in Massachusetts. Her kind
words of encouragement and her enthusiasm in the early
days, together with subsequent provision of historical detail,
were the main reasons behind my decision to research and
write — 'Angels from the Meadow'.

James Stanhope-Brown

This book is dedicated to the memory of
Thomas ('Tommy') Johnson

A true 'Angel' from the Meadow

Thomas ('Tommy') Johnson a former 'urchin' of Angel Meadow who became the superintendent of Manchester's largest Ragged School.

FOREWORD

A letter from America arrived at the Manchester and Salford Refuge and Rescue Society offices during the second week of September 1884. In it, a Manchester woman related the details of a tragedy surrounding three little boys, two of them being former Manchester orphans. The vivid portrayal of this incident captures a story which is unique in the annals of children's social welfare. Not only does she bring to life a part of history in connection with child rescue work on 19th century Manchester streets, but reveals a true account of a group of orphans whose lives were changed dramatically.

At the time of the letter, most of the major cities in the British Isles were coming to terms with the phenomenon of the roaming hordes of street children, the waifs and strays, little beggars and urchins, the 'street arabs'. Often referred to as 'nobody's children', the future of these children was left to philanthropic and like-minded people, who offered rescue and salvation in the name of almighty God. Most of the country's better known Child Rescue Societies were born within this uncertain period, as were Barnardos, The Children's Home, Quarriers and many others. Perhaps because of its rather cumbersome title, 'The Manchester and Salford Boys' and Girls' Refuge Society' to some extent remained in the shadows, but the 'Refuge' or 'Refuges' as it was known locally, pioneered many of Manchester's leading children's charities.

Most people have heard of Billy Graham, a modern day Evangelist who has spent the past forty years or so travelling the world and spreading the gospel. It is doubtful whether another American Evangelist by the name of Dwight L Moody can claim such bold recognition and yet, in his day, Dwight Moody the 19th century Evangelist commanded a similar status during his revival campaigns throughout Europe and the United States. On one such visit to Manchester in the 1880s, a mission designed to draw the masses, Mr Moody came face to face with a small group of children, all of them orphans. What transpired from that confrontation is the theme of this story, and one, which according to D. L. Moody, "had the hand of God in it."

Within recent months there has been public interest and outcry at the almost unbelievable revelation of child deportation which occurred during the latter half of the 19th century, when thousands of young boys and girls fell victim to the philanthropic Evangelists and Government backed schemes of mass emigration. As a result of Moody's timely intervention, twelve boys, whose life stories appear in this book, were given a unique opportunity to resist the inevitable call of the Canadian prairies in favour of a New England education.

Leonard K Shaw, the founder of the Manchester Refuges, is an unfamiliar figure in 20th century Manchester and yet his achievements rank alongside those of Barnardo, Stephenson, MacPherson and Quarrier. As was the case with his contemporaries, L K Shaw answered the needs of Manchester's pitiful street children at a time when their plight seemed desperate. He also accepted philanthropic and government funding for child emigration, a scheme which not only swept clean the city streets but helped in the colonisation of the British Empire.

Jane Newett, the author of the 'letter from America', was a staunch supporter of the Strangeways Children's Refuge as well as being actively involved in many other Manchester charities. A relation of the YMCA Newett family, with roots stretching as far back as early Manchester Wesleyan influences, she continued to labour in the city slums giving whatever help she could to those less fortunate than herself. Although of middle class circumstances with a home bordering the elegant suburb of Bowdon in Cheshire, Jane Newett's approach to the poverty, deprivation and degradation in Manchester proved to be one of immense influence, so much so that her very appearance would open doors and melt officialdom. Sometimes referred to as a 'Florence Nightingale of the workhouse', Miss Newett emanated that special feminine compassion and understanding, a rarity in 19th century institutionalism.

Those same angelic influences together with her Christian fervour were present on the occasion of the American Evangelist's mission to Manchester, when she experienced an unusual sensation concerning the orphan boys, whose fate, it would seem, had been sealed with a heavenly blessing. In the absence of any other explanation, fate found Jane Newett on the Massachusetts landscape at a time when tragedy struck the group of Manchester orphans. It was this incident which caused her to spend an interlude by the Connecticut River, a moment in time as it were, to recall to mind the facts concerning the lives of each individual orphan, and to delve into what she was convinced was a unique chapter in the history of Manchester. The Manchester to Massachusetts episode was a strong echo of personal grief and anguish, a catastrophe which required the Manchester woman to draw from every reserve of her spiritual convictions.

Finally, ... it is hoped the reader will, as I did during my researches, encounter the same amazement and fascination for a story which, although based on fact, never-the less borders on the incredible. It must also be remembered, that when placing this story in its right perspective, one must allow for the Dickensian climate of the last century and the overwhelming influences of Victorianism and 19th century Evangelism.

INTRODUCTION

"One evening, about six weeks before Christmas of 1869 and whilst walking down Market Street towards Blackfriars, I came across a commotion on the corner of Cross Street. Pushing to the front of the throng, I found a newspaper boy lying on the cold muddy pavement, his Evening News and Mails spattered with mud and on the whole looking forlorn and pitiful. The boy, whose cap had found a resting place in the rain soaked gutter, had a familiar look about him and on closer inspection I recognised the city waif whom I knew as Joey Summers, a newsboy who frequented the streets around Albert Square, between John Dalton Street and Peter Street. On learning that he had collapsed with a faint, I arranged for his small frame to be lifted onto a shutter, lent by the proprietor of Beaumont's Drapery Shop. Realising the motive and urgency of the moment, the large crowd opened its ranks to let myself and the stretcher bearers proceed down by Sinclair's to Blackfriars. Soon after this drama, Joey was bathed and put to bed by a good friend of mine, a resident of Deansgate, who promised to care for him until his strength and spirits would allow him to return to his precarious occupation on the Manchester streets.

The next day, it was confirmed by the motherly friend that rapid consumption had overtaken Joey and the pain, like his crying fits, was becoming more frequent and distressful. "It's no good o' me livin", he had said "I'll never sell 'nooses' no more". The woman of the house endorsed the opinion that he could not last much longer and I promised to call again later. On my next visit he appeared to be weaker, from time to time lapsing into bouts of unconsciousness. That night, just before the ten o'clock chimes, he revived and seemed to regain his strength, even to the point of answering a few questions about his background. His father I learned, was dead, and his mother had abandoned him six months ago on his eleventh birthday. When he couldn't earn enough for lodgings he started to sleep out on a regular basis in the handcarts at the back of Mount Street, where, "there was always enough straw and boxes to make a bed." "Just lately," he confided, "av bin goin to Mr Alsop's school in Wombard Street and avin suppers an singin im's." A short pause. "Joey Winters is mi' real name but mi' pals call mi' Summers."

His breathing became more laboured and after a short rest he asked for his pal "Wobbat fwom't Medder," who had gone to fetch more papers "fwom't Evnin Noos' office" at the time of fainting. On telling him that I would pass on any message he had for his pal, he very carefully struggled to take

Shambles, Market Place and Exchange, Manchester.
Drawing: H. E. Tidmarsh.

two soiled newspapers from under his pillow, the last of his stock when he collapsed. After a long fit of coughing and between bouts of breathlessness he said "Give one to Wobbat and keep t'other yersen, its all 'av got to give." After complete stillness for a half hour he suddenly opened his eyes and asked if he could sing. I replied that it might harm him but if he persisted then I would try to help him. "Its a song I learn't at Wombard Stweet afore we 'ad meals;

"Wock o'Bages, keft for me;
'Et me hide myse'f in thee,"

Joey's lisping tongue, his trademark amongst fellow street hawkers, and his genuine concern for his immediate future, made the song sound all the sweeter. Pausing for a few moments, he made another attempt to finish the refrain;

"Wock o' Bages, keft for me,"

In the darkened room and in the flickering glow of the candle, it was obvious a change was near. The words, though now more meaningful, were becoming softer and slower with every breath. In the last line his voice faltered,

"Wock o' Bages, keft for me"

Another pause, and my good neighbour whose tear stained face glistened in the half light, echoed the broken sentence

"Et me hide myse'f in"

A long sigh, and sensing that this was Joey's final offering, my good neighbour clasped the lifeless hands of one whose once anguished face was now at peace, and took up the contribution on Joey's behalf.

Rock of Ages, cleft for me,
Let me hide myself in thee."

This very touching story, witnessed and related by Leonard Shaw, was the key which not only opened the doors to an over sensitive nature and a compassionate heart, but widened the view to Manchester's twilight army of little wanderers.

Soon after this drama and during the same cold winter of that year, two parishioners of the city centre church of St Ann's made their exit from the Queen Street Sunday School. As they stepped down to the pavement they literally stumbled over what appeared to be a bundle of rags lying on the steps. Upon investigation they found the jumble of old clothes doubling for a makeshift blanket which, when removed, revealed two small boys, both of whom were in a filthy condition and both fast asleep. Upon being woken and told that they would be better off at home, the two boys, in true street vernacular of that period, replied, "We ain't got no 'ome."

With the recent tragedy of the newsboy still echoing a sad refrain, Leonard Shaw felt a great obligation to offer some kind of relief and, with a deep sense of pity, he and his friend Richard Taylor each took one of the boys to their home where they provided a warm bath, a meal, and a bed to sleep in.

Both these incidents are now acknowledged to be the awakening of Manchester to its problems of 'street' children. In Leonard Shaw's case, the personal encounter with both the pathetic Joey Summers and the Queen Street 'gutter' children proved to be a blessing in disguise. As he was to

No.16 Quay Street, Manchester. The first Refuge Home.

answer in an interview some years later, "1869 appears to have been a year of destiny in my own case and a milestone in the annals of distressed street children".

This so called 'destiny' was a bold statement from one who was regarded as shy and unassuming. The burden of caring for children over the last decade had earned for him a reputation second to none, and underprivileged children in many circumstances looked to him for their salvation. This was the Leonard Shaw whom Manchester officialdom had come to recognise as the main inspiration behind the rescue work amongst the city's waifs and strays, a man whose quiet strength of character had inspired leading citizens to donate time, money and position to his cause.

'Kilby', as he was known to his closest friends, came to Manchester when he was fourteen years of age, a fact he had revealed when recalling his early life. Having left Dublin and the influences of Robert M'Ghee's Holly Mount Seminary, the family settled in Salford, where the young Leonard Shaw enrolled at St Mathias Church. Some years later as a young business man, he enrolled at the 'St Ann's Square' church, where he became associated with many of Manchester's leading business people, some of whom were to become eventual supporters of the charities in connection with himself and Richard Bramwell Taylor.

This turning point in the life of Leonard Shaw emerged not only at the appropriate time so far as Manchester was concerned, but at a time when the whole of the nation was waking up to the growing demands for social change.

That Leonard Shaw answered his calling at a time when philanthropy was becoming "fashionable" was a most welcome bonus, thus enabling him to create from the word go, a society which was to gain country and eventual worldwide recognition. Having joined the ranks of other ragged school pioneers who had been knocking on the doors of social reform for some years and having heard the pathetic stories from his ragamuffin lodger on the previous night, Shaw arranged a meeting and investigation with his friend Richard Taylor. Setting off along Deansgate after a day's work, they headed for the maze of back streets courts and alleyways between Blackfriars and Campfield, an area spoken of by the two boys as "avin plenty of children beggin' and sleepin' in't streets".

What Messrs Shaw and Taylor found that evening under the dark shadows of city life was a twilight world which teemed with ragged children of all ages and of all shapes and sizes. As the night progressed the squalor and deprivation became oppressive. Ten o'clock had chimed, the hour was late, and yet there was ample evidence of half clothed children on the cold damp streets. Some were without shoes or stockings whilst others, who were not crowding the public house entrance, were selling fuses and begging, with very little to show for their efforts. The duo of Shaw and Taylor drew little comfort from their night's work, knowing that they had only confirmed their worst fears.

Many of the children, the boys in particular, were homeless, and sleeping in empty premises and under upturned baskets was their nightly routine.

In the early hours of the next day, having found sleep interrupted by memories of the night previous and the constant reminder of "Wock O' Bages" Joey, Leonard Shaw drew up a plan which to his mind would help in some way to alleviate the conditions under which most of the children suffered, particularly those of lodgings, hunger and clothing. Having enlisted the help of his friend Richard Taylor they spent the whole of the day canvassing friends and business associates until they had received sufficient support and finance to enable them to begin their new venture.

January 4th, 1870 is a date which is still firmly etched in the annals of child welfare but one which 'Kilby' remembered with a deep sense of pride. "We rented this terraced house in the slum district of Deansgate for a few shillings a week, and between us we cleaned it from top to bottom. The work lasted all over Christmas and New Year but by the 4th of January we were ready for our first customer." The sign written by Leonard Shaw and displayed in the front window of No 16 Quay Street read; "Night Refuge for Homeless Boys." By the evening of the first day ten boys had applied for admission to sleep on wall hammocks and to enjoy a breakfast, every one of them coming from the notorious area around Lombard Street. Covered in vermin and infected rags, the boys had to be bathed in disinfectant and reclothed before prayers were said over a hot mug of cocoa. It seems a coincidence that Leonard Shaw and Richard Taylor should have embarked upon their mission in an area of Manchester where only nine months earlier their friend Alfred Alsop had also encountered the oppressive erosion of social inhumanity. Although unknown to each other at that period, Alfred Alsop in 1869 began evangelising in the slums around Quay Street and in April of that year opened his "mission come gospel room" at 49 Lombard Street. Many months were to pass before Alfred Alsop's determination paid off, but not before he realised that a soup kitchen and second hand clothing handout was the means to a full house and future extension to his missionary crusade.

In the ensuing years, Alfred Alsop's reputation as a 'friend to the poor' took on a new identity. From his humble beginning as a street orator, his mission expanded into a mission hall and soon became firmly established in the very heart of the Deansgate slums. The expansion of the railway companies signalled the end of the narrow streets and alleyways around Peter Street and Quay Street and when the area around Lombard Street was chosen as the site for the

---

BOYS' REFUGE

AND

INDUSTRIAL BRIGADE,

16, QUAY STREET.

Managing Committee.

R. B. TAYLOR, Esq., King Street.

JAMES CHAPMAN, Esq., Westwood, Broughton Park.

L. K. SHAW, Esq., Athol Place, Higher Bronghton, *Hon. Sec.*

Master and Matron.

MR. AND MRS. BROWNE,
16, QUAY STREET.

new Central Station, Alfred Alsop searched in vain for another alternative to his threatened mission hall. As a last resort Mr Alsop and his band of workers decided to erect their own purpose built mission, one which would not only serve as a place of worship, but one which could give warmth and shelter to the poor and needy of Manchester and Salford. In December 1873, Alfred Alsop's mission moved across Deansgate to the new buildings in Wood Street and, with the addition of an extension which was to serve as a Boys' Home, Mr Alsop entered into the business of reclaiming the lives of young children. Although the main purpose of the institution was to evangelise, reform, feed and clothe the masses, this new venture into the philanthropic side of child welfare was to give a new meaning to the growing reputation of the Wood Street Mission.

The symbolic year of 1869, a year fraught with matters concerning children, became highlighted by an event which was reported by the Courier and Manchester Evening News of that year. "The death is announced of one John Napier Armstrong, who died at Hay in New South Wales, Australia. Mr Armstrong who was 35 years of age, died on April 11th, 1869." What was so uniquely outstanding about John Napier Armstrong was his contribution to the ragged school movement in Manchester and perhaps more important, his choice of district, the other Manchester black spot, 'Angel Meadow'. It was here in 1852 that John Armstrong, at the unusual age of nineteen, decided to abandon his well to do Sunday routine at York Street, Cheetham Hill, and spend

every sabbath evangel ising in the squalid neighbourhood on the banks of the River Irk. With a few helpers, John Armstrong not only penetrated the most notorious slum district of Manchester but also established one of the city's first 'Sunday' ragged schools.

In that first year, he rented a room in Millers Lane (now Miller Street) before finally settling for two rented houses in Sharp Street. The first decade under the leadership of John Napier Armstrong proved so successful that Sharp Street Ragged School became a symbol to the supporters of the movement and more rewarding still, obtained eventual membership of the acclaimed Shaftesbury Society. By the time of John Armstrong's disappearance from Manchester in 1867, the district of Angel Meadow had not yielded one inch in its claim to infamy. And yet the episode of Sharp Street and John Armstrong was not all gloom and doom, neither was it a tale of bankruptcy. Perhaps the two most important events to come out of Sharp Street Ragged School were related directly to its founder. *The first*, Henry Charlewood, a lawyer and bachelor from the Crumpsall and Blackley district and a well renowned philanthropist. It was he, who, out of his own pocket, rebuilt the whole of Sharp Street Mission in 1869 from the remains of a disused mill.

The second, concerned Thomas (Tommy) Johnson, a name revered in the Manchester and Salford ragged school movement, and proved to be the more outstanding of the two instances, highlighting a Manchester biography of unequal dimensions. Street life in Angel Meadow, an association with the Earl of Shaftesbury and Doctor Barnardo, and a personal encounter with destitution and squalor before being rescued by the young John Armstrong, are just a few of the episodes which made Thomas Johnson a legendary figure of Angel Meadow. An eventual ally and friend of Leonard Shaw and Richard Taylor, Tommy Johnson was an

Liverpool Road, Castlefield, Deansgate, showing Campfield Market.
Drawing: H. E. Tidmarsh.

ex newspaper seller and street urchin and dedicated his whole life to the poor and needy of Angel Meadow, a fact borne out by his involvement with the first Angel Meadow Ragged School and his promotion to the superintendancy of Manchester's largest purpose built ragged school at Charter Street.

There is no doubting the intensity of the movement concerning child rescue once it had gained a hold in the 1860s.

Perhaps the Scotswoman Annie MacPherson had a claim to its innovation when she began her missionary work amongst the poverty stricken children in the East End slums of London. Her "Home of Industry" at 60 Commercial Street, Bethnal Green, which was opened in 1869, was the culmination of four years' dedicated commitment to the cause of saving and rescuing the thousands of children who begged and slaved and even thieved for their existence. Annie MacPherson and her sister, Louise, made their presence known during the great cholera outbreak of 1866. This time is still remembered by the two Scotswomen as 'the darkest days of their lives' and yet even the overwhelming odds and the dark despondancy failed to deter them in their mission. In effect, the MacPhersons were to jog the nation and the parliamentarians into giving assistance to the scandalous poverty stricken area on their own doorstep. Perhaps it was at the moment during the aftermath of the cholera disaster that the pendulum was to take a long pause, whilst the nation as a whole took stock of the countrywide epidemic of children's social conditions. Never was a time more ripe to prick the conscience of the richest and most powerful country in the world than then, and maybe it was those in-between years of 1867/8 which provided the right conditions for such a crusade and reformation.

It was certainly at this period when Thomas John Barnardo made his entrance upon an East London stage. Annie MacPherson still bore the faded memory of her first meeting with Tom Barnardo many years later. "It was" she recalled, "some time in 1867, when a young gentleman of the audience came to her after the street meeting and offered to help out at her mission." He told her in his Irish accent that he was from Dublin and that, whilst studying to become a doctor in London, he would like to play a part in the local salvation work, to give him the experience for the missionary work in China which was his calling. For such a young person, the MacPhersons recalled how very determined and self assured Mr Barnardo appeared. And yet, on the lighter side of her work, Annie once disclosed to her sister that there was a touch of comedy at the Bethnal Green meeting when Tom Barnardo made his introduction.

"This little man of not much more than five feet and wearing an enormous silk top hat swaggered toward me, displaying his fine clothes and swinging his cane like a young lordship, making it almost impossible to take him seriously." To those who knew the young Barnardo it became evident that, beneath that enormous ego and behind the bright eyes and the neatly trimmed side whiskers, there was a person who was determined to make an impact on society if not

the world. Some people will regret the decision of the China Inland Mission for not accepting Thomas Barnardo as a candidate of their society, but perhaps millions will see this act as a sign from heaven, for there in London's East End at the right place and just at the appropriate time Thomas John Barnardo, 'a man without a calling', stumbled across his own identity.

Just about the time that Leonard Shaw inaugurated his 'rescue society' and 'refuge' in Manchester, a similar chain of events was being enacted in London by Thomas Barnardo, himself a former ragged school teacher. Having temporarily abdicated his medical career in favour of street evangelism and rescue work, Barnardo opened the doors of his first refuge during the Winter of 1869 and within a few months he had rented a second and much larger building in the same district of Stepney, a sure indication of the future of the Barnardo Homes. Across London towards the south lay the notorious district known as 'the Mint' where in 1869 another door had opened and three young men were awakened to the plight of their fellow citizens. The Reverend Thomas Bowman Stephenson, a Methodist minister, who spent some years in the Lancashire town of Bolton and who was entering his second year in the Lambeth circuit of London, had for some time been disturbed at the sight and plight of young boys and girls who roamed aimlessly on the streets around Waterloo Road. Similarly, about that time, two other men who were connected with the Clifton Street Wesleyan Chapel, began a street evangelical mission with the aim of opening a permanent mission hall in the midst of the poverty stricken district. The elder of the two, Alfred Mager, a native of Bath, was certainly the leading figure of the duo and the main influence behind his young friend Francis Horner, a new arrival from Dublin. Between them they outlined a scheme which would not only encourage other business men to finance them but also to seek the blessing of the church. As a result of their newsletter, which appeared during April 1869, Bowman Stephenson knew instinctively that an answer to his problem had been found. The first meeting between Magar, Horner and Stephenson proved to be an instant success, with Bowman Stephenson achieving the support he needed for the proposed Boy's Home. Within three months a house at No. 8 Church Street opened its doors to the first little boys, George and Fred, both of them 'mudlarks' of Lambeth marsh. By March the following year Thomas Bowman Stephenson proposed that a suitable title should be placed above the entrance to the successful venture at Church Street, and after studying all the implications, decided on his own interpretation which was simply: "The Children's Home".

Whilst London's East End was benefiting from the early efforts of Scotland's Annie MacPherson, Glasgow itself was about to benefit from the growing achievements of one her countrymen, William Quarrier. As a boy, William Quarrier and his family moved to Glasgow from his birthplace at Greenock and, as a result of his father's death and the destitution which followed, was compelled to live in the slum areas of the East End, close to Trongate and Salt

The 'Shoeblack' Brigade marching to their work destinations in and around Manchester are seen here on Great Ducie Street, Strangeways.
Drawing: H. E. Tidmarsh

Market. It was here in the notorious Wynds of Glasgow that young Quarrier began his career as a journeyman shoemaker at the age of twelve years and followed his trade in and around the tenement areas of the city. By the time William Quarrier had reached his fortieth birthday in 1869, he had built up a chain of shoe stores and boot-making shops. However, it was not the material wealth and achievements that brought fame to William Quarrier, but rather his other enterprise of rescuing street children. Even before the endeavours of Anne MacPherson, John Barnardo, Leonard Shaw and Mr Stephenson, William Quarrier's strong sentiments as a practising Christian Baptist were brought home to him on a cold November evening in 1864.

In an account of what transpired, Mr Quarrier once related his story to Mr Shaw and described how he had taken pity on a street boy a match seller in Jamaica Street, who had been robbed of all his stock and was crying bitterly at the prospect of starvation. William Quarrier described how, that night after the incident, he decided to take up the cause of the Glasgow street children and sent a long letter to the Editor of the Glasgow Herald at around Christmas time of that year. With a plea to the business gentlemen of the city, he described his visits to London and the successful Shoe Black Brigade which was in operation there and his intentions of starting a similar venture for the boys of Glasgow.

By the following year, the Glasgow Shoe Black Brigade had become firmly established and in succeeding years was followed by the uniformed boys of the Newspaper Brigade and Parcel Brigade. Knowing of the philanthropic contributions which were being performed by George Muller at Bristol, and of Annie MacPherson and John Barnardo, a decision by William Quarrier to contribute to the ever growing needs of Glasgow's street waifs produced his second historic newspaper appeal in August 1871. Urged by Annie MacPherson to open a children's home, Mr Quarrier, through his supplications to the Christian citizens of the city, was able to lay the foundations to what was to become the universally acclaimed Quarriers Homes of Scotland, which were officially opened in 1878.

CHAPTER ONE

Jane Newett
C/o Mr Moody's Home
Northfield
Massachusetts, USA
27 August, 1884

My dear Kilby,
*   This letter, my first since crossing the Great Lakes and ar-*
riving on American soil, was intended to be a revelation of the
wonders of God's creation, which are so abundant on this big con-
tinent. Instead, and while the thing is still clear in my mind, I am
writing to tell you about such a sad little history which happened
at Mr Moody's Boys' School this week. Yesterday a picnic was
announced for the children of the Sunday School, to be held at
the Boys' School. During the morning Mr Moody started over
there to make the arrangements. Ethel and Emma (Moody), and
the boys had also gone over there for a walk. As Mr Moody ap-
proached, he saw a number of boys running down to the river-
side. He hurried on and asked if anything was the matter. Someone
answered 'three boys are drowned'. Mr Moody tore down to the
river bank and got a boat, and went down to where they said they
had sunk. An American Indian boy who was a splendid swim-
mer dived for them and found them all, but too late they were all
gone. When the children got there, the cart was being pulled up
the hill, bringing the bodies of the poor little boys. Mr Moody came
before them looking the picture of death, and said, "If you don't
wish to meet them, turn away." I think you will want to know
of this tragedy because two of the little ones were our 'disciples'
from the Manchester orphanage......

Searching for the right words and pausing for a long
moment, I reflected on how unreal this whole episode seemed. Here I was, sat amidst the tree lined hills of
Massachusetts, overlooking the shining Connecticut River
and the distant outline of the New England states of Vermont and New Hampshire. The fragrance of the forest, ac-
centuated with the heat of summer, and the peaceful serenity of this beautiful location of Northfield and Mt. Hermon,
made it possible to hide behind nature's refinery. And yet,
because of the severity of the incident, there was no hiding
place. Manchester, in England, was at this moment a million
miles away, but somehow time and distance were meaning
less and my thoughts were now drifting with the smoke and
smells of the Irk and Irwell. Just over twenty one days ago
I had set off on a business cum holiday journey across the
Atlantic, the purpose of the trip being an escort to twenty
Manchester Boys who were emigrating to Canada and the
Western states. This sojourn at Mr Moody's home at Northfield was my reward, as well as being my first ever official
holiday, and it seemed only fair that my benefactors at the
Strangeways Children's Refuges should now be the recipients
of my thoughts.
*   You will be glad to know, I'm sure, that I was at the funeral....*
Another tear began its downward journey, as once more I
made an effort to continue the letter to Kilby. It was painfully obvious that I was in no mood for writing down what
had to be told and yet the obligation on my part was overwhelming. Wiping my eyes with a handkerchief which had

long since outlived its absorbent qualities, I wondered for
a moment whether, twelve months earlier, Mr Shaw had
spent some of his quieter moments at this very spot. It was
beautiful, this setting amongst the tall pine trees; a little acre
in God's heavenly garden, so pastoral and picturesque. Just
over a year ago Leonard Shaw had come to this place from
England "a Manchester man", it had been claimed, "who
had witnessed a miracle." My own feelings were hesitant
when the question of miracles arose, but there was no denying that this whole episode over the past months had contained so many celestial influences. Perhaps more to the
point, Kilby had played a significant part, if not a major role,
in that so called miracle for, without his guidance, his principles and his committed dedication, none of this would
have happened.

Retreating still further in time, I remembered coming
across those first entries in Kilby's diary, notes written by a
young man who had visibly mapped out his future course and
taken the helm of his ship.

"**January** 5th, 1870; Walter Thurlow Browne and Emma
Browne of Norwich arrive today to take up the post of Master
and Matron at the Quay St. Home, having previously served in the London Ragged School movement." There was
nothing unusual about this first entry except to acknowledge
that Mr Browne was related to Sir Thomas Browne, a well
known author of East Anglia. However, at thirty years of age
and with a donation of basic school room equipment from
Mr Heywood and a selection of books from Mr Rylands, W
T Browne took on the almost impossible task of School
Master cum Industrial Teacher and Religious Advisor to the
Deansgate 'street arabs'. Those first few months were vital
to the future of the Quay Street mission and it was a very
grateful Mr Shaw who shared in the triumphs of W T
Browne's contribution during those trying times. Speaking
together during a day excursion to Longford Park on October
the 8th, Kilby thanked Mr Browne for his efforts which had
by now produced the nucleus of an 'industrial brigade' and
the beginnings of a boys' 'Drum and Fife Band'. Later that
afternoon, during an interval when Mrs Rylands was enter-
taining the twenty-four boys to tea and buns, Walter Browne
related a story to Kilby which not only impressed the wide
eyed listener, but was to serve as an inspiration to his future
work amongst children. The story made known to Leonard
Shaw was one which concerned the children of London, a
sad and depressing tale, magnified by its awful truth. During this sojourn in Stretford, Leonard Shaw acquired first
hand information of his 'East End' counterparts in the
metropolis. Names of several institutions came to light but
two in particular were to remain uppermost in his mind. Not
surprisingly, that of Doctor Barnardo of Dublin came to the
fore and Kilby searched his memory for some reference of
his fellow Irishman. Frustrated in the attempt, he turned to
the Scotswoman, Annie MacPherson, a person who he had
been told was like a young Florence Nightingale, tending the
needs of the poor and sick children of the London slums and
evangelising to the masses.

Leonard K. Shaw founder member of the Manchester Boys' and Girls' Refuges.

Yes! There was a general agreement that Walter T Browne, together with the influential help of a few Manchester businessmen and the foresight of Leonard Shaw and his friend Richard Taylor, had laid a firm foundation at the Deansgate 'refuge'. By the time the first anniversary had been reached, the house at No 16 Quay Street was unable to cope with the never ending stream of so called 'street waifs'. Such was the success of the Boys' Refuge with its various industries of 'firewood making', 'shoe-blacking', 'newspaper', 'parcel and messenger carrying', boys who were now coming from the Angel Meadow and Salford hideouts were being refused admission. In true business-like fashion the end of year meeting contained some new proposals as to the obvious expansion of the Deansgate work and it came as no surprise when L K Shaw put forward a motion at the meeting on 20th March to purchase two houses which he knew to be empty and on the market. He suggested that numbers Ten and Twelve Frances Street, Strangeways, purchased and fitted out by April 1st, and agreement was unanimous. The question over Mr Shaw's choice of district as the new headquarters of the Refuges would always pose a controversy over the years to come. Surely a home and refuge in the suburbs would have seemed an obvious choice to most people and there was no denying that a street like Frances Street which bordered on the gaol perimeter and Red Bank was a last resort. It was true that Leonard Shaw had been toying with the idea of a move towards the Salford side of Manchester knowing full well that any vacuum would be catered for by the Lombard Street

Mission and his friend Alfred Alsop. However, it was at this crossroads interval that the 'way ahead' was revealed to him.

Leaving St. Ann's Square with its rank of horse-drawn cabs, Leonard Shaw, in the course of his business pursuits with the Scottish Life Assurance Company, accidently collided with Mr Sowler, the proprietor of the Manchester Courier newspaper.

On recognition of each other, having become acquainted through the fellowship of St. Ann's Church, Mr Sowler took hold of Leonard Shaw's arm and nudged him in the direction of the news vendor on Corporation Street. "There is a young gentleman whom I would like you to meet, and in view of your contemplations concerning a children's refuge, it might be to your advantage." Pointing out the rather thin and poorly dressed youth who was shouting "curyers and nooses, second edition," Mr Sowler went on; "his name is Tommy Johnson and he was reared in Angel Meadow. There used to be a woman who was responsible for his welfare; he doesn't remember having a father or mother, just a brief memory of his family having been taken from him during one of the epidemics in Angel Meadow". After a brief introduction Mr Sowler made his departure and left Leonard Shaw to carry on the conversation.

Already familiar with some of the legends in Angel Meadow, Leonard Shaw, in his philanthropic capacity, was held captive by the young man from the Meadow who described in great detail and from personal experience the awesome background to his existence. What became obvious to Mr Shaw was the genuine sincerity of Thomas Johnson, a young man who was so knowledgeable of his ill reputed environment and who so badly wanted to improve his situation. His graphic biography revealed a district in Manchester which not only surpassed the Deansgate reputation, but pinpointed a city slum which cried out for refuge and rescue. Tommy had known and still remembered some of the Ragged School teachers at Sharp Street and Charter Street and had a much clearer memory of the 'soup kitchens' and the 'Christmas Day treat'. At this point, Leonard Shaw realised the true sincerity of young Tommy Johnson and after learning that he forsook his living on Saturdays and Sundays in favour of helping at the Charter Street Ragged School where hundreds of children sought help from starvation and destitution, the future of his mission work became apparent.

2nd May, 1871, the diary read .... Removal completed to Frances Street.

10th May, New sign erected on gable end of No 10 Frances Street. 'Boys Refuge Industrial Home' Committee! R B Taylor, L K Shaw, Jas Chapman.

Wednesday 31st May, Took all the boys in a waggon to St Anne's-on-Sea.

Tuesday 7th November, First meeting of Trustees today: Messrs. John Rylands, Herbert Phillips, Ald. Pearson, Richard B Taylor, Jas. Chapman, Leonard K Shaw.

The Bishop of Manchester, Doctor Frazer, was present at the meeting and observed the trustees as they formulated a draft copy of the first ever deeds and principles of the

Refuge. In effect they outlined the society's rules in the following order:

"To receive homeless and destitute children found in Manchester and Salford district.
To give immediate admission to such without distinction or creed.
To provide such with suitable food, clothing and Industrial training.
To educate such in Christian principles based on the Bible only."

When relating those early years, Kilby had once confessed to me how much he had been influenced by a man who he thought to be a saint amongst men, "a sort of silent partner" he had remarked, "a father figure and a gentleman with a kindly countenance." To those who were familiar with the philanthropic societies, the Ragged School movement, and Manchester's evangelistic missions, only one person fitted this virtuous description. At eighty-one years of age and with a definite 'Old Father Time' look about him, Thomas Wright, the well known prison philanthropist, still played an active part in befriending the homeless and destitute children around the streets of Manchester and Salford and his conventional dress of top hat, long black frock coat and walking stick were easily recognisable. It was easy to see why Kilby referred to him as being saintly, an expression which even Lord Shaftesbury had uttered after one of his meetings

with Thomas Wright. Now that the Refuge had established itself on Thomas Wright's patch so to speak, a much closer relationship was forged between the old man of Strangeways and the boys at the Home in Frances Street.

Before the year was out, Mr Wright had expounded on the idea which Mr Browne had nurtured from his days at the London Ragged Schools and between them they succeeded in organising a uniformed Manchester Shoe-Black Brigade, an institution which was to serve as a future foundation of the Refuge. Thomas Wright I learned, was a living legend. Well known for his personal involvement with the reformatories and prisons, he devoted all his time to what he termed his 'pet cause', "the reclaiming and befriending of those who had gone astray." Not surprisingly his commitment and service to his fellow man had brought Government acclaim and recognition from the country's leading philanthropists, not least of whom was his special friend Lord Shaftesbury.

The simmering heat of New England and the agility of the hillside insect population was beginning to distract and annoy to such an extent that I conceded my resting place and sought refuge further inside the pine forest. The tear stained letter, a painful reminder of my present obligation, stared back at me and failed completely to make further contribution.

I wonder whether Kilby still remembers that cold December evening in 1874 when he and I walked from Peter Street to the Refuge. A damp heavy fog had followed us

No. 10 Frances Street in the 1870's. Note the rescued boys engaged in the industrial 'firewood making' activities.

through Long Millgate and Ducie Street and it had been a relief to find a comforting open fire awaiting our arrival. I can remember the searching expression on the faces of Mr Browne and Richard Taylor as Kilby slowly thawed himself in front of the embers and then drew up a chair. "Tonight I met Mr Moody," Kilby declared, "and tomorrow he and Mr Sankey have agreed to give some time to our cause." A simple enough statement by any standards but there was no doubting the sense of achievement which was shared by the committee on hearing the news. The great American Evangelist who according to the press reports "had set Manchester on fire," was now committed to the Manchester and Salford cause of raising money for the homeless and destitute children of the city. Dwight Lyman Moody, the thirty seven year old evangelist from Massachusetts was engaged in his second British tour of mission work which had just begun in November. Never before in the history of Manchester had people queued in their thousands to listen to a man of God who appeared to be successfully spreading the Bible message. The great revival movement of the British Isles pioneered by Mr Moody had caused an awakening to christianity which had not been witnessed for over a century.

Beginning in York and Newcastle a year earlier, Mr Moody and his songster partner, Ira D Sankey, had progressed to Edinburgh, Dundee, Glasgow, Belfast, Dublin, Sheffield, Liverpool, Birmingham, London and Bristol. As a journalist so aptly put it, "Manchester, I rejoice to say, is now

Thomas Wright often referred to as the "Lancashire Howard" on account of his prison philanthropic work.

on fire. The most difficult of all English cities, perhaps, to be set on fire by anything but politics, is now fairly ablaze, and the flames are breaking out in all directions."

As in all cities of England, Scotland, Ireland and Wales, Moody and Sankey were to leave a legacy towards the future of Manchester which would be written into the history of the city. Speaking at his first rally at the Free Trade Hall, where every seat and every inch of standing room had been taken up hours earlier, Mr Moody said, "I believe God is about to do a mighty work of grace in Manchester." From that meeting in Peter Street he went directly to the Oxford Music Hall in Oxford Street where an overflow rally had been organised. By the close of Moody's first convention in Manchester, it was estimated that no less than twenty thousand people had attended the city rallies and yet the ebullient young Moody was growing impatient in his belief that the masses of Manchester citizens were still untouched. In a carefully worded letter to the newspaper, which was aimed at the popular Saturday evening and weekend columns, the following publication appeared:

"To the Clergy of Manchester and Salford. Having come to Manchester with my friend Mr Sankey, for the month of December, with the one object of Preaching Christ, it has been a matter of disappointment that not more clergymen of the Church of England have attended our meetings. As God has granted large blessings where unity has prevailed, we earnestly trust that you will join in seeking a blessing for Manchester. Signed D L Moody, Manchester December 4th, 1874."

The second week of Moody and Sankey according to a local journalist was "a most strange phenomenon." Thousands of people who were unable to gain entrance to the overflowing Free Trade Hall had subsequently filled the alternative venues of such buildings as the Oxford Hall, Cavandish Chapel, Rev A McLaren's chapel on Oxford Road, the Roby Chapel and Oldham Road Wesleyan Chapel.

My first meeting with Dwight Moody is one which still stands out as one of my memorable moments in life. As organiser of the Hospital Flower Mission and Pillow Mission Society, I was invited to attend the rally at the Free Trade Hall where a collection for Manchester charities would take place at the close of service. Never in all my years had I witnessed so many people inside and outside the great hall, there must have been a conservative estimate of twelve thousand. I had been fortunate to gain admission to what was to become Mr Moody's acclaimed Manchester address, "How to be a Daniel," an inspiring speech which was aimed at the teachers of Day Schools, Ragged Schools and Sunday Schools. It was some time after Mr Sankey had concluded the mission with his hymm singing, that I made my way to the meeting room to meet the two Americans. The quiet spoken and mild mannered Mr Sankey with his receeding hairline was the first to shake hands. He had, I was to learn at a later date, met Mr Moody at a YMCA conference at Indianapolis in 1870 and had given up a well paid government position in Newcastle to join in partnership with his col-

This 1873 photograph is without doubt the most unique picture ever recorded in the history of the Boys' and Girls' Welfare Society. Note the upturned Shoe Black boxes used for seating.
NB: Thomas Wright died two years after this photograph was taken.

league. Mr Moody, the leading force behind the revival mission, was in every way that I had imagined, a powerful man of medium height with a square face and neatly trimmed black beard. Some people had referred to Dwight Moody as an uneducated Chicago farm boy with a brusque manner, whilst on the other side of the street at the Theatre Royal, a music hall burlesque artist had mocked the two evangelists. Mr Moody was a simple man, a man who possessed an overwhelming personality and a gentle and compassionate nature. It was easy to see why Lord Shaftesbury had taken to him when they had come face to face in London in 1867, for it was at that conference that Mr Moody's unconventional attitude and unorthodox freshness had been accepted by the English society.

Dwight L Moody, the story goes, came to his ancestral homeland in 1867 with the sole purpose of meeting the two people who he reverently held in admiration, Pastor C H Spurgeon, the well known author of religious sermons, of London, and George Muller of Bristol. Of Mr Muller, Dwight Moody had commented on the way that Ashley Down Orphanage for one thousand five hundred children was financed by God, a reference to George Muller's well known habit of praying whenever he needed money for his cause.

When I look back now at that first introduction to Mr Moody and reflect on the benefits both to myself and to the community as a whole, I am reminded of those news columns which followed in the wake of Moody and Sankey's departure to Sheffield.

"Messrs Moody and Sankey left us, for the present at least, on the afternoon of Thursday, New Years Eve of 1874. For four weeks in the darkest, coldest and dreariest season of the year, have these men of God toiled amongst us with an amount of dilligence and zeal such as I have never seen equalled, far less surpassed. The results have been amazing. To speak figuratively we have had a summer in the depths of winter........."

"During these five weeks God has answered the prayers of many years, and we cannot but feel that what has been going on in the city has made Manchester peculiarly interesting to the dwellers in heaven.........."

"The hold which Mr Sankey's melodies took on the population of Manchester, and the rapidity with which they spread from Europe to the very ends of the Earth, constitute a phenomenon which has scarcely ever been paralleled; and we believe that long after the earnest, stirring words of Mr Moody are forgotton, such hymns as 'Safe in the arms of Jesus', 'The Ninety and nine' and 'The Home over there', will remain to give comfort to the children, the young and the old."

Both you and I will always remember the last week of Mr Moody's Manchester tour.

Looking up Peter Street to St. Peter's Square. The buildings on the right include the Free Trade Hall, Theatre Royal and YMCA.
Drawing: H. E. Tidmarsh.

This loud reflection and pause, in my letter to Kilby, took me back to the day after Boxing Day when in front of the vast audience of the Free Trade Hall, I was presented with one hundred and fifty pounds towards a New Year gift for every orphan child in Manchester and Salford. For Kilby, those last few days of 1874 held a special significance in relation to his one interest outside the realms of child philanthropy.

For some years Leonard Shaw had actively played a part in the growing movement of the YMCA, an interest which brought him face to face with some of Manchester's leading young businessmen. At the time Mr Moody came to England, the Manchester Association were desperately looking around the city for a permanent home at a price they could afford. What transpired from a chance remark by Leonard Shaw to Mr Moody during his mission became the talking point for months after. An observer of this historic episode reported the sequence of events. "At nine of Wednesday evening, about three thousand men assembled in the hall to hear what Mr Moody had to say on the subject of the Young Men's Christian Association. Mr Herbert Spencer occupied the chair and gave a brief address, intimating that the Association would like to purchase suitable premises in the city. They had been looking at a dingy looking old public building just a few yards away from the Free Trade Hall. The former use of the building as Manchester's Natural History Museum had ceased when it's contents had been transferred to the magnificent Owen's College. The asking price of thirty thousand pounds for the old Museum seemed beyond the reach of Manchester's estimated seventy thousand young men but the undaunted Dwight Moody with a first hand knowledge of the YMCA in America, gave an inspired speech in which he appealed for all the Christians to donate to the future of Manchester's spiritual well being. At the end of the meeting, Mr Moody urged the young men of the city to secure the building in question, for the Association. As a result of that conference, two thousand three hundred pounds was collected, making a total of eight thousand pounds which had been received or promised.

On Monday last, the old museum was purchased for the YMCA. Within two days of its security, part of the building giving accommodation to about five hundred persons was seated, lighted with gas and heated; so that on Wednesday night, Mr Moody used it to hold an overflow meeting from the Free Trade Hall."

This was the finale to the Moody and Sankey campaign and sadly it was to be nine years before they returned to Manchester. When they did return to England in 1882/83, their visit to Manchester was preceeded by a report in the monthly magazine of the Refuges. In fact, Kilby, as I remember, was one of the committee which placed the notification:- "Moody and Sankey are with us again; and will probably ere long be in Manchester. We never have been and are not now enthusiastic admirers of the manner and methods of the two eminent Evangelists — especially the former of the two. We venture this remark with much diffidence, but we know our

Dwight Lyman Moody — in later life.

readers will not take it for one ounce more that it is worth, and we only offer it lest it should be thought that our blind admiration of the two men had warped our judgement." My own reaction to this statement had been in inward smile, probably because, as Kilby's friend, I was only too aware of his wholehearted enthusiasm for the American Evangelist. What was it that he had once remarked? "Dwight Moody has a vision, which gives him an awesome power to motivate the masses. Like Bunyan, he had the great gift of being able to realise things unseen and to describe his vision in a simple language."

How astonishing, — even to my conservative attitude the next visit of the two Americans turned out to be. Not one person who knew the workings of the Manchester and Salford Refuges would ever dispute the events which occurred during the first two weeks of March 1883, nor the subsequent episode of the 'Twelve Easter Disciples'. The editor of the Christian Worker initiated the sequence by referring to the forthcoming visit of the two well known evangelists. "Moody and Sankey are to make a brief two week mission to our city, beginning on March 1st. The numbers who have been flocking to hear them in Birmingham and other places (twelve thousand and upwards), makes us doubt the capacity of any room in Manchester, to accommodate the numbers who desire to hear them. However, the Committee have engaged the Free Trade Hall, the Circus in Chepstow Street, and the YMCA buildings." When the same editor publish-ed the synopsis of Moody and Sankey's two week visit to Manchester he could hardly have been aware of the so call-ed miracle which had taken root at the Strangeways Refuges, and which was about to blossom at the Cheetham Hill Orphanage.

"The twelve day mission by the two American Evangelists has been brought to a close. From the beginning, the largest halls of our city were filled to capacity. During the last days of the mission, the doors of the Free Trade Hall were besieged for hours and no sooner had the doors opened than every seat and standing place was occupied. A second meeting had to be arranged at the Chepstow Street Circus and then another overflow meeting at the YMCA. Had the buildings been three times the size, they would have still been too small to accommodate the vast crowds who came from all parts of the city. This is without precedent in the religious life of our city, and we look in vain for an ade-quate reason for it. A plain, earnest man comes amongst us — he is untitled and unordained, he has neither that com-manding presence or those gifts of oratory which would make him out as "a king amongst men." What is there in this to move our city as it has been moved? We believe that there are abler men and sweeter singers in our midst than the two of whom we write, and yet, these two men have held thousands, day after day spellbound. We say this cannot be explained by any human chain of reasoning. We cannot come to any other conclusion other than that the "hand of God was in it."

How accustomed I had become to hearing that phrase. I had heard Kilby utter it on three occasions, and Mr Moody on as many more, the most recent being yesterday at the funeral service. I was still finding it extremely difficult to come to terms with what had taken place over the past twen-ty four hours, especially when I looked back to those March days and the commencement of this story. The dimensions of this tragedy, probably without equal in my lifetime, were awful, and those recurring echoes from Manchester such as "The Angels from the Meadow" and "Mr Moody's twelve little Disciples," rose to a deafening crescendo amidst this peaceful Connecticut River Valley.

Inside Free Trade Hall, Manchester. Drawing: H. E. Tidmarsh.

"Open the door for the children
Tenderly gather them in
In from the highways and hedges
In from the places of sin."

This well known Refuge motto which was positioned over the doorway entrance, indicated that you were about to enter the city centre branch home of the Boys and Girls Refuge. Situated in Major Street, and surrounded by warehouses, the home was regarded as the house of hope and shelter for the little wanderers. During the early years of the society, a friend of Mr Shaw's, the Rev. E Hewlett, wrote a summary of the day to day workings of the mission and went on to say:-
"London and other great cities had provided open-all-night shelters for the fallen, but so far as we know, Manchester was almost the first, if not the very first to provide a shelter open night and day for the little ones."

There was no mistaking the sincerity behind the words of Mr Hewlett but what each sentence failed to convey was the immeasurable heartache attached to each stroke of the pen. If only the committee could turn the clock back and foresee the tragedy which had brought the institution to its knees on that bitterly cold November evening in 1878. Tommy Stephens, a thirteen year old street boy and his ragamuffin pal Willie Teesdale had presented themselves at the Major Street Shelter in the hope of finding a night's warm lodgings. They were penniless after having spent the late hours trying to sell some newspapers and waxlights around Piccadilly Infirmary, and now tired and hungry and in tatters on a dark cold night, they found to their dismay that ten o'clock was past the hours of admission. Mrs Philbean, the matron, was sincere in her apology and promised to help the boys when they returned the next day. For Willie and Tommy, the following day was never to dawn.

In their bid to find warmth and shelter, and in the absence of a threepence to secure a doss in Angel Meadow, the little wanderers tramped Ashley Lane and Red Bank up to the Brickfields at Cheetham Hill. The Evening News was to reveal this story to a stunned committee at the Refuge when they read with horror, how the two orphan boys had been overcome by fumes and had died as they slept in the warmth of the factory chimneys. Very rarely did Leonard Shaw allow his feelings to surface, but on hearing of this catastrophe he personally accepted the blame and admitted that with his knowledge of child rescue work, he was very much at fault. Sometime after this incident the Rev. E Hewlett composed a poem which was circularised throughout the Manchester Missions, two verses of which, eventually taking place within the entrance hallway of the Major Street Refuge:

'The Open Door'
"Oh type of the door of mercy,
'for ever open and free',
Of the dear Lord's word of welcome,
the loving "Come unto me!"

For even the vilest sinner,
desolate, guilt stained, poor,
May come to the house of mercy,
and pass through "the open door."

On type of the heavenly city,
that stands in the land of light,
Where the pain can never enter,
and the wrong is all set right.

For the gates of that blest city,
'are shut not night or day'
And the ransomed people enter,
'and they that enter, stay."

As I remember, it is fifteen years since that brief interlude at the Quay Street Rescue and Refuge home and now, the Society's extensive buildings and homes are acknowledged as being the future foundations to the ever growing 'childrens' charities' for Manchester and Salford. Only recently an eminent biographer wrote "When the history of the philanthropic work of the nineteenth century comes to be written, a prominent place will have to be given to the Manchester and Salford Boys and Girls Refuges. The object of the Institution is; 'to receive and provide for all homeless and destitute children found in the streets of Manchester and Salford, to train them up to gain for themselves, an honest living, and above all, to win their hearts for the Saviour'; or as it is expressed in the trust deed: "to help those who are willing to help themselves."

The same biographer in his more recent appraisal of the Refuge, gave an account of the workings of the Orphan Homes. In a touching introduction which described how the Orphan Homes had begun with two houses in Johnson Street off Queens Road in 1874, he went on; "Nothing in creation is so hopelessly helpless as the human infant, and, with the universal sympathy felt for those bereft of the natural ministers to their wants, it is little to be wondered at that provision for their hearts should be found in all directions. There are at present six homes, four for boys and two for girls.

We visited them a few evenings since, and not often during our peregrinations have we been as much charmed and delighted with what we saw there. They are situated in George Street, Cheetham Hill; stand all together, side by side, differ not at all in outward appearance from ordinary respectable houses; and each has a strip of flower garden running down to the railings in front, with trees overhanging the side walk. Behind the houses is a plot of field for outdoor amusements, and at the back of all, lies Broughton Park which ensures a permanent supply of healthy fresh air, as can be obtained within so short a distance from the city. With flowers on the tables and toys scattered on the floor, a stranger may be misled into thinking, he had been admitted into the bosom of an ordinary family. Two things would no doubt puzzle him, the large number of children and the comparative youthfulness of the mother. With twenty children to each home the much bothered 'mother' must feel like the little old lady who lived in a shoe.

Then as to the appearance of the children themselves. Undoubtedly we thought we had never seen a finer, healthier, more frank-eyed lot of children anywhere: a tribute to the system devised by Mr Shaw and Mr Kirlew. The secret lies in the thoroughly home like life they lead, the absence of all uniforms or badges and the constant care to keep from them anything in their dress or environment which would remind themselves of their origin. To this end, instead of being educated on the premises, they are sent to the school of St John's and are dressed as are other respectable children of their own age.

The histories of most of these children is sad enough, and most have lost both father and mother. It would be as well and for their sake if all the children were orphaned and in the same position, for the great fear is lest any surviving parent should make their appearance and put in a claim. We talk much of breed and of blood, but certainly no-one not in on the secret would ever suspect the sea of misery and destitution out of which most of these fine youngsters have been drawn."

Writing an official letter to Kilby — albeit painful — was one thing; explaining the Connecticut River tragedy to the Orphan Home mothers was a duty I dare not contemplate at this moment. Theirs would be a special grief, a mothering grief which I had personally carried for them since learning of the River disaster. My own involvement with the Orphan Homes began almost two years ago when I was invited to attend the official opening of the George Street homes by the Bishop of Manchester and Mrs Frazer. Following the crowds of visitors on that November weekend in 1882, I walked from Cheetham Village and turned left into the respectable thoroughfare where the six houses met my view. Later in the afternoon when the crowds had thinned out and the ceremonies had given way to the normal routine, I sat down at the table with the boys of No 4 home, where I had been invited for tea. On reflection, I now realised just how significant that day at Cheetham had become in relation to what had happened yesterday. Some of those very same boys who were now a part of the Northfield setting, were yesterday's well mannered and well dressed lads who so obediently rendered the graces of that dinner table.

In the vernacular of the Refuges and Mr Moody, No 4 Home of the Cheetham Orphanages was were I met my first 'disciple'. During a conversation with the home mother Mrs Whitelaw, I learned during that evening of the various incidents and circumstances which had befallen the children and how they had qualified for orphan status. In the cosiness of a warm glow from an open grate and the contentment of a satisfactory day, I listened intently as the home mother related a story concerning one of her ten year old boys, known as Johnnie Collins.

Johnnie's was a sad tale and like most of the others he was rescued just at a crucial time in life. What was different about Johnnie was his shy polite ways and his innocence of mind, not at all like most of the street lads. The thing which

had given him away and made Mr Shaw pursue his interest into the lad was his peculiar accent which was most definitely not Mancestrian. About the time Mr Shaw came across Johnnie, was when the committee at the Refuge were out on the streets of Manchester, compiling notes on the hundreds of underage children who were being used as 'street hawkers'. As I remember, Mr Shaw was trying to get a bill through parliament, or something like that, and he was collecting evidence to show the city of Manchester how little tots were being employed by parents as night traders. Well anyway, Mr Shaw came across Johnnie, and so taken was he by what transpired, he wrote a sort of essay which he intended using in the Refuge's monthly paper. At this point I half smiled. I remembered the tract which Kilby had written concerning the 'little wanderer' from the South of England.

Leonard Shaw's story — a touching one I recalled — came back to me. Taking a sip of hot cocoa which had been served up by the house servant I reflected on Kilby's portrayal of 'Shude-hill Johnnie', a nick-name he had used to characterise his young subject.

"It was eleven o'clock one Saturday night when we found ourselves wandering leisurely along through Shudehill Market, where weary stall holders, even at that late hour, were calling out their wares and merchandise. What a history this Shudehill market could give to the world. It would astonish even those bargain hunters who throng together in those crowded isles, intent only on their own passions. Who has not been in this busy market on a Saturday night and mixed with the throng, elbowing your way through whilst being almost deafened by the continuous shouting of the vendors. There is a strange mixture of humanity here, as there is in all markets. It is a small world in itself. There is almost every type of character here, from the big blustering publican who stands at his door with the hat on the back of his head, his red shining face wearing the most self-satisfied smile, whilst his hands deep down in his capacious pockets jingle the money he has, down to the pale. A sharp featured baby tries to sell its few flowers or matches to the passerby. There is the poor wife trying to lead home the drunken husband and sad to say, a husband too often intoxicated himself, trying to support his wife — truly 'the blind leading the blind'. From the young girl in all her flaunting finery, to the young mechanic looking around for a 'boiling of green', or even a gaze for a moment at the 'book worms' peering into the secondhand books at the corner stall.

Leaving the larger stalls and the wealthier owners, we descend to the lower strata of the motley crowd, and casting our eyes about, see what might almost be taken for phantoms or shadows of human beings who, in croaking, sepulchral, or shrill voices, endeavour to dispose of the four articles at the bottom of some old basket. We have the hoary head, whose owner totters with uncertain steps, and tells in unmistakable language that life's journey is nearly over, and at its best has been but a clouded one.

Passing by the Cheap John's, broken down musicians, the dumb man who can speak, the blind woman who can see, and the clean meek looking (sham) widow, with a large family of borrowed children, we note more especially the vast number of boys and girls, varying in ages from four years to fourteen, who, as you pass them, follow with a persistency quite astounding, under your feet, behind, before, and with the usual cry, "Please buy". To a thoughtful observer, how painful is the sight!, the wasted form, the stunted growth, the pale thin face, the large pleading eyes, the garments like so many torn ribbons fluttering in the breeze, and trying to cover a deformed or emaciated body. Such children are termed 'Gamins', street children, city arabs, gutter children, and many other choice names. Poor creatures!, they are the children of negligent parents or guardians and hence they are left to the wild tossing of life's tempestuous ocean alone, until some friendly hand is stretched out to save them. Street children have now become an important subject, engaging the attention of the highest in the most exalted positions of society.

Now that the philanthropic cry of "Save the Child, Keep the Child" is heard and with that same view in mind, we took our Saturday evening walk through Shudehill market to hunt up any case that might be found, for it must be known that Shudehill and the surrounding neighbourhood is the rendezvous for city 'arabs' and hungry lads.

Winding our way slowly through the various stands and stalls, keeping a sharp look out, we spied a likely catch. He was a lad, apparently ten or eleven years old. He moved stealthily like a lone hunter, looking under each stall that he passed to pick up anything that might have fallen off. Poor lad, evidently he was both cold and hungry; his ragged coat pinned close up to his throat, his cap drawn tightly over his head. From beneath the peak of his cap a pair of dark eyes gleamed forth; first fright, then timidity, betrayed themselves as he warily looked around. His hair was long and matted; he had evidently been some time in the streets, and was cer-

tainly, as he afterwards put it, "out o' luck." Having settled in our own minds he was the right one to get hold of, and with a considerable amount of caution we approached him, not sure whether he would 'bolt' or stand his ground. We placed our hand gently on his shoulder, and said "My lad, you look in a bad way!" He gave a start, and was about to run, whereupon, laying a firm hand upon his shoulder, we said, "Don't be afraid; we are friends and want to help you."

He stood still; a sad pensive look settled on his face, and heaving a deep down sigh, he said, "Thought you were the D's (Detectives) or t'Board (School Board). As a small knot of curious people began to gather around we motioned the lad to follow us, and strolling along so as not to attract attention, made our way to the livestock corner near the Rover's Return, where there were a few passers by, and where the following conversation took place:-
"Have you a mother?" "No Sir."
"A father?" "He died, Sir."
"Run away from home?" "No Sir, from lodgings in the Meadow."
"Do they know where you are?" "No Sir."
"How long have you been on the streets?" "Six months, Sir, sometimes with my pal."
"What do they call you?" "Johnnie Sir, Johnnie Collins, Sir."
"Come now Johnnie, what do you say to a good home, warm clothes, plenty of food, a bright fire and a happy future with a new master?"

For a few anxious moments there was silence. After what seemed an eternity, tears began stealing down those cheeks; the light of other days flitted before his youthful mind, and the present cloudy and uncertain future hung over him oppressively. A deep drawn sigh signalled the end of his struggle and he whispered, "For my father's sake, I'll go with you Sir."

The 'Rover's Return' Shudehill.
Drawing: H. E. Tidmarsh.

"Thank God, thank God, my lad for that," we said, as we took his hand in ours, "there's a bright future in store for you, and an honourable manhood, if you do but trust in God and do the right."

It was now very late, past midnight, as we wended our way to the Home. The wind whistled and blew the poor lad's scanty rags as we walked as rapidly along as his tired, sore limbs would allow us. He shivered as he said in his southern accent, "My, but it be very cold, Sir." Before long, the Home and 'Ever Open Door' in Major Street was reached. The kind smiling matron led us through to the kitchen where a bright cheery fire seemed to welcome the Shudehill wanderer. After a warm bath and some clean clothing Johnnie came for his supper, looking every inch a frail cherub in his gleaming nightgown.

Once settled at the table he gazed openly at the pile of hot buttered toast and the cup of hot delicious coffee. He looked up at us but could not speak, at least not in words, his heart was too full of emotion. A deep rooted sob which shook his little frame erupted into a deluge of tears as the matron clasped Johnnie to her bosom. Just at that moment when words seemed lost, we gazed at the lovely and appropriate verse which adorned the living room of the Home:

"The look of sympathy, the gentle word,
Spoken so low that only angels heard;
The secret act of pure sacrifice,
Unseen by men, but marked by angels eyes:'
These are not lost.

The kindly pain devised for others' good,
So seldom guessed, so seldom understood;
The quiet steadfast look that strove to win,
Some wanderer from the ways of sin;
These are not lost.

Not lost oh Lord, for in the city bright,
Our eyes shall see the past with clearer light;
And things long hidden from our gaze below,
They wilt reveal, and we shall surly know;
These are not lost."

"Do you think you will be happy here?" we asked him as he was going up the stairs for his bed. "Yes Sir," he replied. "We'll ask God to help you and he will be your guide. Now, good-night, or rather morning. I hope you will sleep well, and have pleasant dreams." I was to learn from Mr Kirlew, some months later, that Johnnie Collins slept soundly for three days after his admission to the Refuge and had in his own words, "been so happy and content I felt afraid of waking up and finding it all to be a dream." When I inquired about Johnnie's background Mr Kirlew smiled as he proceeded to explain the circumstances. "Johnnie Collins isn't his real name, its a nickname given to him by his pals who couldn't be bothered giving him his full title. His proper name is John Collings Caton and he comes from Portland in Hampshire. His mother died when he was three years old and his father, an ex Army man and a Smith by trade, came to Manchester to find work on the new Town Hall constructions, where he died. Johnnie was left in a lodging house in Angel Meadow and survived for nine months before we found him." The rest of the story I knew, having spoken to Mrs Whitelow, who still persisted in referring to him as Johnnie Collins, so as not to confuse him with the other two Johnnies of the home.

The John Collings Caton I had come face to face with yesterday and today, was a very different version to the Manchester days. One of the heroes of the disaster, John had matured in mind and soul, as well as physique, and like the other Refuge boys, had acclimatised to the Massachusetts landscape. Yesterday's burden was unbearable. Another tear fell on an already soiled notepaper. Was it only a year I wondered, since Kilby himself had spent that interlude at this very place, penning that beautiful descriptive letter of Northfield Mount Hermon and telling the happy news of his so called 'twelve disciples'? I pondered on this observation for a while and cast my mind back to that day in the city office of the Refuges in Corporation Street, a day when all the editions of the 'Christian Worker' had all been sold up on account of the local interest in the 'American Letter' and it's good news concerning the orphan children.

CHAPTER THREE

Northfield
Massachusetts,
USA
11th June 1883

"Are the Manchester boys here? Yes, here they are. How are you boys? A hearty welcome to you." These were the words that greeted our ears as the cars of the Connecticut Valley Railway drew up at the Northfield Station. It was quite dark, past ten p.m. on the night of Saturday June the ninth. But there was no mistaking the voice, the last time we heard it was six weeks before in Liverpool, swaying to alternative smiles and tears and some seven thousand people and here he was; for it was Mr Moody's voice we heard, having driven some distance, accompanied by his brother, eldest son and daughter, to welcome to a new land a little party of emigrants twelve orphan boys from the Orphan Homes of the Boys' and Girls' Refuge, Strangeways.

It was, indeed, a welcome voice after ten days in the Atlantic Ocean, on board the good ship 'Cephalonia' of the Cunard line. We had made land in the early morning of this day, and under a bright and burning sun, with the sea like glass, we had sailed up Massachusetts Bay and into Boston harbour. This was followed by nearly five hours in "the cars", so that our boys were tired and weary at the close of a hot and exciting day, and like water to a thirsty land was the cheery voice of our friend, whose guests we were to be for two or three days.

Our boys were soon up in one team, their luggage in another, and off they drove to the Boy's School, some three miles away, while Mr Moody's conveyance carried us to his pretty house at Northfield. It was difficult to realise that we were between three and four thousand miles away from the scenes and associations of all our previous life and work.

The special object of this letter is to tell of Mr Moody in his home and in his work at Northfield, where, in one sense, he "dwells among his own people." The name seems indigenious to the soil of the place; there he was 'raised'; there in the home on the hill still dwells 'his mother'; his brothers also live in the adjacent houses; while more distant relatives are scattered over the lovely Northfield district.

As you walk or drive along the road you will notice that he knows everyone, and has a suitable or friendly word for each. To one it is a remark as to the church or prayer meeting last Sunday, to another it is a question about the crop in yonder field, to a third comes a query as to buying that young and promising horse, whilst to the fourth and fifth, there are anxious consultations respecting the Girls' Seminary and the Recitation Hall at Northfield, or as to the supply of water to the Boys' School at Mount Hermon; for Mr Moody is not only an authority on church matters and the work of God throughout the world, though that is nearest his heart, but he is great on farming, knows 'the points' of a horse, is well up in farm stock generally, and is, as we say here, "a good all round man". Very pleasant was it to notice his friendly greetings on the road to the church, or at the foot of the church, that great rendezvous for all country people.

But any account of Mr Moody at Home must be an account of all educational agencies which he has established and carries on, and which we think are destined to make Northfield as famous in the future as Yale or Harvard at present.

First, in point of age and importance, is the Girls' Seminary. Occupying an elevated position at the North East end of this long and pretty town, and commanding a splendid view of the Connecticut River and Valley, this institution is in striking contrast to all round it.

The houses (each detached and surrounded by its own neatly-kept plot), which line both sides of the long broad street and compose the town of Northfield, are wooden structures, built very much like Swiss Chalets, and look very bright and neat in their coats of white and green, with a magnificent background of mountain and forests. Mr Moody established this some time ago in order to give a higher education to respectable young girls of good ability, whose parents could not afford to give them a regular coverage charge. A small sum per annum is charged, sufficient to secure a respectable class, while it is not allowed to exclude any who have the requisite fitness and preparatory training, the object being, to prepare these young ladies for teachers in schools, as governesses, and for missionary and evangelistic work in the Church.

In this handsome building, and in another pretty wooden house lower down, dwell some hundred and forty young ladies ranging from fifteen to twenty years of age. Their course of study extends over four years and includes Music, Logic, Latin, French and German. Every Sunday afternoon in Summer a most interesting sight is witnessed. These young ladies are seen wending their way, in groups of twos or threes to one of the beautiful slopes on the hillside, near the shade of some trees. Each carries her Bible, and frequently a little note book. Mr Moody and his family are seen climbing the hill from his house below, and then, seated on the green grass, surrounded by some fifty to one hundred young people, "both hearing them and asking them questions", Mr Moody is indeed "at home". A hymn or two is sung, and sung beautifully, for music is studied at Northfield.

A short prayer is offered, and then follows a most instructive Bible lesson. We had already, in the afternoon, at Northfield Church, at Mr Moody's request, given some account of the work in Manchester amongst orphan and destitute children — but Mr Moody's heart was touched by the sight of twelve orphan boys arriving the night before from England. He referred to them in the morning service, and had prayed very beautifully for the 'little disciples', but still he wanted to hear more, and so, he begged us to tell a little more about the children, the 'rescued children' in the Manchester home.

When Mr Moody heard that twelve pounds per year would support a child, he suggested to the young ladies that they support an orphan in the Manchester Home. This cause was promptly taken up and "Alphy Brown" was "adopted" by the Girls' Seminary at Northfield, as their boy — a most unexpected but very practical result of this truly interesting Bible class.

A very large congregation assembled at Northfield Church on this Sunday morning. Every seat was occupied, and it being intensely hot, fans were in large request. We were struck with the large number of men all well dressed, substantial looking people. We did not see a poor person in the town. The service and Sunday School over, the people returned to their homes. A prayer meeting for those living near the church, closes the day which, for Mr Moody is an extremely busy one. He is an early riser, and of course retires early. He says "he likes to go to bed when it gets dark". It was so on the evening in question but he was up early in the morning at five o'clock and had harnessed his favourite horse and was off; by seven thirty he was back, having been to the Boys' campus on the other side of the River. Breakfast and prayers are over by eight thirty, for at that hour he meets the young ladies of the Recitation Hall, a neat brick building not far from his house. Having set the wheels of the large masses at Northfield in motion, with the oil of prayers, and leaving the various studies to go on under the direction of the highly trained lady teachers, Mr Moody hurries off to the Mount Hermon campus.

This is where our hearts were, for our boys were there — those bright and happy companions of a ten day ocean voyage. So, of course, we accompanied Mr Moody. A pleasant drive in his buggy, of about five miles, crossing the river to the opposite side of the valley, brought us to Mount Hermon, where on a farm of about four hundred acres, stands five new houses. They are close together yet detached, built of fine red brick. They are most substantial houses, of combined swiss and gothic style. They stand in a splendid situation, a thick wood behind.

This 1890's photo shows the completed Cottage Row at Mount Hermon. The second building from the right was the house occupied by the Manchester 'Twelve'. In its present day, the House is still referred to as 'Manchester'.

The hillside on which they stand, slopes gently down to the river, where on the other side lies the Northfield range of hills, well and richly wooded. Our twelve Manchester boys were the first to inhabit one of these newly built houses, the only one finished, the other boys who were already there, still occupying the two pretty farmhouses until the new ones were ready.

Each house will contain a Matron, a teacher and about fifteen boys, and here, surrounded by the cows, sheep, pigs and fouls, and all the appliances for tilling the ground and cultivating the fruits of the earth, which abound here in their season, the work — the alternative work — of educating the mind and developing the muscles of the body and brain will go forward. Here, our boys from Manchester are placed, and from here, as they grow in years and develop in mind and heart, and above all, as they grow in grace, will these twelve go forth to scatter "the seed of the kingdom" and bear the "glad tidings" to the dark places of the earth. A neat school is built a few hundred yards off, with all the appliances for an efficient education.

Such is a brief outline of Mr Moody's work "At Home". We left Northfield, and "our twelve" that same night, leaving behind us a part of our hearts, for we can never forget the Manchester boys whom we had known and cared for, for so long and who had been to us like sons.

Before leaving our friend, from whom we received such kind hospitality, we could not help expressing the thought which had been growing in our minds every hour since we came. That as important as his evangelistic work was, and none felt its importance more than we did, we believe the educational work going on at Northfield and Mount Hermon is more important still, as we followed in thought each of these girls and boys going forth to be themselves centres of light and love, and healing, preparing the way for that kingdom which shall — "stretch from shore to shore, till suns shall rise to set no more."

ed Schools and City Missions, were the solemn faces of Leonard Shaw, Richard Taylor, Thomas Johnson, Alfred Alsop, Mr Le Mare and Thomas Brittain.

The thousands of spectators who had witnessed the funeral on that Spring day had contributed to the memory of an outstanding citizen.

To me the event had been more personal. When I saw the red coated boys of the 'Shoe Black Brigade' marching in front of the City Mission contingent I was aware of the Thomas Wright I had met at the Refuges, a grandfather

Looking towards Blackfriars and Strangeways from Chapel Street, Salford. NB: St John's Cathedral on left hand side. Drawing: H. E. Tidmarsh.

Less than a month before this publication, I had been a spectator at the Easter-time funeral of one of Manchester's most loved and respected citizens, Thomas Wright, the so called prisoners' friend. It took place on a Saturday afternoon on April seventeenth, at the Birch Church of St James, Rusholme, and according to the hundreds of mourners, was "the largest Manchester had witnessed for years." Beginning at the Roby Chapel, just off Piccadilly near the Infirmary, the procession made its way down Portland Street to Oxford Road and then continued to Birch Park, a route which traversed the Sydney Street home of the Wright family. Leading at the front were the bands of the Barnes Home and the Drum and Fife Band of the Refuge, who alternatively played the 'Dead March'. In true traditional Victorian splendor, the boys of Ardwick Industrial School preceeded the sixteen horse drawn carriages which conveyed the relatives and VIP mourners, amongst whom was Canon Stowell of Salford, the Rev. Willis of Roby Street Chapel, Canon Bardsley, Captain Leggett, Governor of the Salford Hundred Prison and Mr Richard Johnson. Standing outside the Hippodrome, I was able to view the spectacle which stretched for over a quarter of a mile and, there at the front of the cortege leading the two hundred representatives of the Ragg-

figure to the boys, who all knew him affectionately as 'Mr Jingo', a nickname given to him in the first place by his friend Mrs Gaskell the author, for his continual use of the phrase — 'By Jingo'! Perhaps more clearly, I can see him taking his place amongst the Band boys come Shoe Blacks in readiness for the first ever group photograph to be taken at Frances Street, a picture which now adorns the panelled wall of the committee room at the Refuge. Quite fittingly, the last words quoted in an obituary by a national newspaper at that time, were by Lord Shaftesbury, the friend who had attended the Guild Hall ceremony in London, in order to receive a special presentation of Thomas Wright's portrait — "We shall do well to pray without ceasing for an ample succession of Thomas Wright's."

All of this past history had come back to me for one particular reason. With the present Mount Hermon disaster still uppermost in my thoughts and the Manchester boys claiming my attention, I was reminded of Joey, another of the 'twelve', for it was on the day of Thomas Wright's funeral that a four year old boy had been received at the home at Strangeways. Joseph Dooley, I was to learn at a later date, had been deposited at Frances Street by his fourteen year old brother who was at this point leaving Manchester to find work. Having recently lost his father, through bereavement and the mother ill at Crumpsall Infirmary, Mrs Browne had been given no alternative but to shelter the little waif who seemingly had no present home to go to. Dishevelled and dirty, Joey, a typical 'meadow' boy from Charter Street, spent some nine months at the Johnson Street Orphan Home before being reclaimed by his mother. This episode concerning Joey was just another case in the day to day running of the Orphan Homes and ordinarily, his recorded details would have accumulated with the thousands of others and become filed away in history.

Joseph, as verified by the Wood Street Superintendent had left the Refuge Orphan Home to join his mother who had remarried. After an unsettled period of two years the sick mother had died, leaving Joey with his stepfather Mr Old, a man who earned his living as a vagrant labourer.

"This man wanders about with a little child of his own and does all he can to lose and get without Joey," Mr Alsop had said, "he left him in a street in Hyde near to his grandmother, and again in Gorton near the gaol." About six weeks ago Joey was left on the Piano Shop corner of Deansgate near Cupids Alley, and told to wait until the stepfather came back. According to a pal of Joey's a boy who lodges in Spinningfields; "he met up with this strange lad on Deansgate and stayed with him until it got dark and then took him home to his mother." We know that the mother was in a desperate situation herself and could hardly maintain her own child, let alone another whom her son had befriended. Our first encounter with Joey was at the time of the daytrip to Southport when, Mr Hayworth the schoolboard officer had eyed him with a degree of suspicion when he was queing with the other lads outside the Wood Street Mission. Later in the day, Joey caught the eye of Mr Alsop, who had observed the young boy on the return trip to Manchester and, in his opinion, "was acting very strange" In the crowded train compartment, Joey had managed to isolate himself in a quiet recess and unlike the rest of the boys, had crouched on the floor clutching tightly to one of his stockings, which you would have thought contained all his wordly possessions. On asking him why he had taken his stockings off and what the contents were, he replied, — "Mi mother's never seen't seaside so 'ave shuvvel't some sand in mi stockin' to show 'er." Two days after this incident the worried 'mother' called at the Mission and begged us to take little Joey as she couldn't bring herself to turn such a loveable boy onto the streets with the other ruffians."

Thankfully, eight year old Joey was returned to the fold as it were, and eventually settled into his new Orphan Home at Cheetham Hill. Although 'easily influenced' as the Home Mother put it, "Joey is quite unmistakeably the most likeable boy in the Orphanage and always has a smile for everyone." Yesterday the matured Joseph Dooley had displayed a composure beyond his years and today's mourning had stilled the once happy face of youth to a heart breaking lament. And yet, for good reason, Joey had cause to acknowledge that he himself had been spared from the Connecticut drowning, and along with Johnnie Caton had become a Mount Her-mon Hero. My memories of Joey at the Manchester Orphanage were of a popular young boy with an accomodating disposition who always became a favourite at Christmas time, a boy who, because of his Christmas Day birthday, caused his smile to broaden into an infectious grin for the duration of the festivities.

"The Meadow." Still deep in thought and completely absorbed in far-a-way bustling Manchester, I reeled off the names of those of the twelve boys whom I assumed to have an association with Angel Meadow. There were seven who had direct links and possibly another two whose meanderings had circuited this notorious district of Manchester. London, I had been informed, had equally distressing neighbourhoods and so too had Glasgow, Birmingham and Liverpool. The thought that there might be another half dozen 'Angel Meadows' perturbed me.

I had been informed that the Meadow district had become twice the misery of the Deansgate slums and that metaphorically speaking, Manchester's largest lodging house area was sinking into the iniquitous quick sands of the River Irk. Numerous stories had been written about Angel Meadow, most of them elaborating on the dark abyss of the city, where the partnership of gloom and doom accompanied the marjority of its inhabitants. There had been moments in the past when I had tried to form my own opinions of the Meadow, and mental pictures I had drawn were derived from tales repeated to me by patients and their relatives at the workhouse and Infirmary at Crumpsall and Salford.

Some years ago, I had taken the first prize in a poem recital competition and to this day I can almost remember the whole of the many verses composed by my favourite author. True, the matter referred to the abuse of children, and the period in which Lord Shaftesbury was presenting his ten hour charter for working children, but here on the streets of Manchester, Elizabeth Barrett Browning's "Cry of the Children" was still a reality. The last verse in particular was never far from my lips, especially when I encountered the children at the Wood Street and Charter Street Ragged School dinners:........

"They look up, with their pale and sunken faces
And their look is dread to see,
For they mind you of Angels in high places,
With their eyes turned on Deity! —
'How long' they say 'How long, Oh cruel nation,
Will you stand to turn the world, on a child's heart, —
Stifle down with a mailed heel it's palpitation,
And tread onward to your throne amid the mart'?
But the child's sob in the silence curses deeper,
Than the strong man in his wrath."

Taken in 1900, this now famous photograph belonging to the author's Robert Banks collection, captures the inhabitants of Angel Meadow awaiting the arrival of a Duchess, to officially open the extensions to the Charter St. Ragged School and Working Girls Home.

CHAPTER FOUR

"The very mention of the name "Angel Meadow" (in Manchester), causes a grin to rise upon the face of the street boy, to make the passers by shrug their shoulders and officialdom to shake its wise head. In the old days their cry was — "Can anything good come out of Nazareth?" So with Angel Meadow. Could the noble band of Ragged School teachers speak, or the clergy of St Michael's tell; then the disbelieving outsiders would hear of many a brand plucked from the burning hell of this place. On entering Angel Street from Rochdale Road and quietly walking down its deep descent (indicative of a social sliding scale), one is struck with a peculiarity which cannot slip the observation of the most cursory observer. It is the common lodging house quarter of Manchester. They are on every hand. It is —
lodgings to the right of them,
lodgings to the left of them,
Yes, by the hundreds.

Almost every house sports the legend — 'Lodgings for travellers'. Here one can get a night's sleep for four pence and no questions asked. Of course, it is money down on the nail. Mine host acts on the principle — "short reckonings make long friends". Many of these 'hotel des voyagers' are in such a bad state of repair, that a liberal use of whitewash and paint would certainly make them look all the brighter and smell the sweeter."

These were the words of Mr Browne of the Refuges, who from time to time had cause to visit the Charter Street and Sharp Street Ragged Schools. However, my favourite narration of Angel Meadow was without doubt that of the Rev. Adam Scott, a friend of Leonard Shaw's who had acquired the services of Thomas ('Tommy') Johnson to act as his escort.

"Two years ago I had come to be Minister of a surburban church. The work was interesting and there was always plenty to do. Albeit, I was continually casting my eye upon the neighbouring city of Manchester, with its great needs for earnest Christian Ministry.

I was resolved not to allow myself to be shut up in a 'cupboard of respectability', indeed it has always been my dreams that the church which I had come to serve should, with me, enter some thorough mission work in one of the dark places of the city. From time to time passing along the street, I had witnessed some of the 'sins and sorrows of the city'; but the desire to see more was presented to me and lately it was gratified.

An appointment was made for me to be taken through some of the darkest districts. Two nights were fixed, a Saturday, because there are sights on that night which are not so visible as any other, and also the following Tuesday.

It was arranged that the friend who was to act as my guide and protector — for let it be understood, that as I was to visit the thieves' quarters, it might not have been safe for me, a stranger, to have gone alone, even if I could have piloted my way — should wait for me at a little "all night shelter" for children, in Major Street.

But see, here is my guide, with a beaming face that tells me I am welcome and that he is willing to do for me all that I want. I am not at liberty to give his name, but it is "written in the Lambs' book of Life" and with it not a few other names of those who he has plucked as "brands from burn-

Angel Street, Angel Meadow. Drawing: H. E. Tidmarsh.

ing". He was born in the district we are about to visit; he remembers neither father nor mother. A poor woman took him into her home and he became 'her boy'.

His 'photo' when a child is before me. There he stands a proper 'city waif' without boots or stockings and without hat or jacket. What a boyhood was his! What scenes of wretchedness he must have endured, but when he was twenty his heart was won to God and old habits abandoned. Ever since his conversion he has lived in the same locality. For quite a number of years he has served with fidelity one of the most respectable firms in Manchester, who know and appreciate his value. He lives and labours among his old friends for their good, and if he had twenty lives they would all be spent in the same places and amongst the same class.

And he has his reward, he is trusted, respected and loved. It did one's soul good to observe the many hearty recognitions he met with as we moved on together and how the children caught hold of him and named him. I was told I was quite safe in his company, and had reason to believe it. Not an uncivil word was spoken to us; we had not an angry look given us, and no thieving hand was laid upon us to do any injury.

The first halt we made was opposite an immense public house known as "The Beggars Resort". Here, it is understood, a very large percentage of the money received in begging on Manchester streets finds its way; and I was told that a previous landlord had retired from the business, in the possession of a handsome fortune. Several women in the most wretched condition, in rags and dirty and dazed with drink, hover about the doors. One of them has a pair of black eyes — one out of about a score of women which I saw during the night in the same condition. At a little distance off there is a free fight going on between two brawling factions, which was not the only thing of the kind I witnessed on our peregrinations.

From this point we move on towards Angel Meadow proper, abounding in lodging houses and, alas; not a few dens of iniquity. In all this district, with its hungry thousands, I did not see a single handsome provision shop, but the temptations to drink are manifold. Its dwellings are mean and poor in the extreme, but at its head there stands a gin palace upon which no expense has been spared. It is lighted with electricity, and made in every way tempting for men and women who love their drink, to enter. In the centre of Angel Street — one of the chief lodging house streets — there is another public house known as 'The Angel Inn' and which, though not so pretentious, draws into its coffers a goodly share of "the poor man's pence."

We halt at the door of a large lodging house in Charter Street, which has 398 beds, at prices from threepence to sixpence a night. There might be two or three hundred men in the house, several of whom I am sorry to say, were tipsy.

It was hard to believe that some of these were human beings, harder still to believe that they had been made in the image of God, and were capable of becoming saints in the kingdom of Christ. My friend speaks kind words of these poor men. He tells them the old story of the love of God,

and gives them a hearty invitation to his Sunday evening service at his Ragged School and Mission.

A little further down the street we enter one of the smaller houses. On entering the kitchen we have soon a goodly congregation around us of all ages, from the babe of the breast to the grandma of seventy years. And yet, what a curious crowd it is, marked by poverty, dirt and untidiness. Boys are here with men's coats on, the tails of which all but touch the ground with their sleeves tucked up; without stockings or shoes, bareheaded and unkempt, and face and hands as if they had maps outlined on them in sepia.

Down at the foot of the hill near Ashley Lane, there faces us two superscriptions that once arrest our attention. One is this: "No drunkard shall inherit the kingdom of heaven," and the other is: "Jesus came to save and seek the lost." They are painted across a large and good-looking house which is "The Boys' Rest and Coffee House", belonging to the Boys' and Girls' Refuge. In former years much of the drinking in the neighbourhood was done in this house known to the locals as "The Old Victory". My guide tells me that when he was a boy, many a night he lay under a form in one of its rooms, whilst men and women danced, drank and gambled. In those days it was a gate of hell to youths; now it is a gate of heaven. The public house has been turned into a coffee tavern and a place of protection for homeless boys and gives hope to penitent souls.

As we stood in the bedroom my friend pointed to the right, and said to me, "You see those two beds, I came here one night a few weeks since and found them occupied by two young brothers. Their respectable appearance told me that they did not belong to the class that usually comes here and I was right in my surmises. Fortunately, they have been taken into the Orphan Homes at Cheetham Hill."

From the 'Boys' lodgings, we went to look at the lodging house for working girls and young women — another most useful institution, right in the heart of the locality. Here young women, for threepence per night, can find a comfortable bed and, what is more important, perfect protection from the hand of the destroyer. In the same building is the "Ragged School". It has, I believe, a thousand scholars on the books, and an average attendance of 750.

It seemed to me, as we wandered along Charter Street, that the young women were the greatest sufferers — that they, more than any others, experienced how hard is the way of the transgressors. We saw them at all stages of that way. One of these was seated on a doorstep in Crown Lane and drinking beer, evidently to her delight, from a large cracked mug. Our guide knew who she was, and informed me that she was just beginning the life of sin. Turning the corner into Long Millgate, we found another young woman, also sitting on a doorstep. Her eyes were swollen, they had been black and were getting better. There was a terrible woebegone expression on her face and great tears coursed down her cheeks. On another doorstep, in Gould Street off Pleasant Place — who invented these names of beauty, I wondered — we saw a woman nursing her baby son. Poor woman! She sobbed as if her heart would break. She was the inmate and victim of

One of the alleyways off Corporation Street adjoining Angel Meadow 1908. Courtesy: City Engineer, Town Hall, Manchester.

W. T. Browne's artistic attempt to describe a few of the 'Angels' of Angel Meadow in the 1880's.

a house of iniquity.

Alas, alas! for the slain of the daughter of the people!! And how cruelly and wantonly in her thousands she is being slain. In Angel Meadow we saw sights we could wish with all our hearts we could never see again and there too, we saw sights to make us grateful and glad, for there are lights in that dark district, lives consecrated to God and spent in his service. The name Angel Meadow is suggestive of fields begirt by hawthorn hedges and woodlands; but if ever the district presented so pleasing an aspect, as probably such was the case, then how changed it had become".

Before I had begun my journey to the American continent, another campaigner, the Rev. Mercer of St Michaels — Angel Meadow, had attended a special meeting at the Strangeways Refuges. One of the speakers at this first ever assembly in Manchester in connection with the growing national movement of the Society to prevent Cruelty to Children, was Mr Moreton, a city dweller, who resided at No 7 Lower Mosley Street. It was on his suggestion to Leonard Shaw that the Boys' Refuges should form an association with Mr Gilbert Kirlew to spearhead the movement on behalf of Manchester; Mr Kirlew being a former labourer of the Children's Aid Society. Since the death of Mr Chapman in 1882, Gilbert Kirlew had become a committee member of the Refuges and had further become instrumental in the major decision making in the newly formed Cruelty to Children Society, his vast experience as Manchester's representative of the Children's Aid Society proved invaluable. However, it was the Rev. Mercer's vast and indepth knowledge of his own district which contributed to the initial policies of those early days of the "Society".

Such were the revelations of Angel Meadow during the course of his speech that I became amazed at what little I did know about the district which had captured my feelings. The mood of the meeting having already absorbed a powerful and emotional contribution from Tennyson, grew decidedly quieter and sober with each naked truth of the Angel Meadow. —

"Is it well that while we range with science glorying in the time,
City children soak and blacken, soul and sense, in city slime?
There among the glooming alleys, progress halts with weary feet,
Crime and hunger cast our maidens by the thousand on the street,
There the master scrimps his haggard sempstress of her daily bread,
There a single sordid attic holds the living and the dead;
There the smouldering fire of fever creeps along the rotten floor,
And the crowded couch of incest in the warrens of the poor."

St. Michael's Church Angel Meadow — viewed from Angel Street.
Courtesy: Chris Makepeace.

In his statistical summary Mr Mercer continued:-
"Angel Meadow forms a square with Rochdale Road, Miller Street, Cheetham Hill Road and Gould Street. It contains about 33 acres which support about 7,000 people. The density of the whole area is 300 to the acre, and is on a par with the metropolitan slums of St Anne's Soho, Whitechapel and Bethnal Green. In England and Wales there are 497 persons to the square mile while Manchester had 26,350. In Angel Meadow the total number of persons is 192,000.

Along Old Mount Street there are pillars and dignified flights of steps at the main entrances of the houses. In Long Millgate there are some half timbered houses in good preservation, which evidently once overlooked the river, when the valley below was yet a pretty sight, and when the walks along it out to Blackley were among the most pleasant around Manchester. There are many living who can remember St Michael's as a 'carriage church', and now it is practically unknown. Some may remember St Michael's Flags where beneath lie the bodies of thousands of plague victims, and now serves as a children's playground. The highly unnatural conditions of life in Angel Meadow are well known to have

a lowering effect on human vitality. The air in the houses is bad, that in the streets is not much better. And yet in these houses and streets thousands are born, live and die. We may well add 'die' for the death rate of Angel Meadow is 50.9 per thousand per annum. The average for all England is less than 19. Only the strongest can live, and those who do live, do so on a lowered scale of vitality. On the question of immorality in the district, based on 42 streets of the parish, only 15 are free from this class. The state of two principal streets show that, out of 54 houses in Angel Street, only 8 are quite free, whilst Charter Street has only 21 houses free out of a total of 79.

Lastly, we have to think of the children of the slums. Their case is one of the saddest with which we have to cope. Who shall describe the lot of the children! Neglected from birth, thrown on their own devices while still infants, initiated early into the worst secrets of vice and crime, insufficiently warmed, clothed, fed, what chance have they? The hearts of those who work in Angel Meadow often bleed to watch the children as they develop day by day. Home life they have none, and the most natural affections and sentiments are blunted or repressed. This, then, is Angel Meadow, once a wealthy district, with the Georgian Houses and Porticos, nestling amidst beautiful scenery and with undulating landscape views and trout stream. Now, these once stately residences are occupied by common lodgings and doss houses."

When the Rev. Mercer closed his lecture, he did so in the customary fashion by concluding with a suitable verse illustrating the significance of his address:

"Thou who are the Lord of all the tender pities
Mercy incarnate, human and divine,
How can we write the name upon these cities,
Where in thy children live like herded swine,
Would not those eyes, that saw those Angels gazing
Into the brightness of the Fathers' face,
Turn on this slum with love and fury blazing
Shrivelling our souls with shame of such a place."

Whilst summoning these events to memory, and recalling the special incidents which placed each one of the boys into his own individual category, I remembered thinking of two of the 'twelve', whose circumstances had differed from all the others, in as much as they had benefited from the love and devotion of an older sister. "On the night in question," wrote Mr Richard Taylor, "we arrived at this common lodging house on one of the low streets of Angel Meadow and clambering up a dark and broken down staircase with a bit of candle in an old bottle, to make some light, we came to the top and pressing a latch, entered a large empty fireless room, where on the floor covered only by the rags of clothing which they wore, lay a boy and his sister, huddled together in a garrett, in order to keep the cold out. There was not even the proverbial three legged stool, — an old broken box served for chairs and table for two! And so they had survived for weeks, — mother in the workhouse Infirmary, father dead!"

Chapter Four

Mr Taylor's account in 1880 of the story concerning this boy and girl was one which I knew intimately, and one which served to inspire Mr Browne to put pen to paper for the first volume of the magazine produced by the Boys' and Girls' Refuge. I had been requested to escort the girl, — on what turned out to be a bitterly cold and wet November morning, — across Cheetham Hill Road and Redbank, to the newly formed "Working Girls' Home" in Nelson Street. There, in the comfort of the warm parlour room overlooking St Michael's Flags, the story of Martha and Edwin Cartledge unfolded. For some three years or more Martha, now sixteen years of age, had in the absense of her mother managed to eke out an existence, and by taking on the role of head of the house had managed to keep both herself and "baby" brother Edwin out of the workhouse. In her own words, the sadness of their short but hard life revealed a tragic childhood, where the two of them had managed to pay for the lodgings in the garrett room. Sometimes the mother had returned home for a spell and occasionally her older brother would come and bring some money. According to Martha, "all went wrong when an Uncle died at his lodgings and there was only the "Nooses" and "Mails" and waxlights to keep us in food and lodgings."

"On that day," went on Martha, "when school was finished at four o'clock, I handed over the last five boxes of matches which had been left over from the night before, to little Edwin, while I rushed off to the publishing office of the Evening News. As usual, my brother said he would go instead, on account of all the rough lads scrambling for the papers and me always getting my feet trodden on and full of cuts and bruises. If I thought that he wouldn't listen to all the swearing and cursing and wouldn't learn any of the bad habits, I would have stayed on the street. After dividing the papers in two we met up at the coffee stall near Sinclairs, just like we always did at seven o'clock at night. When Edwin didn't show up I went looking for him and found him on Market Street crying with his face black from the ink. When I asked him and his friend what was up, he pointed to the bundle of "Nooses" at his feet covered with a piece or rag. "No-one will buy mine now," said Edwin. When I asked why, his friend said, "Edwin was giving this gentleman a paper when he snatched it and told him to be quick and upset the lot. When he picked them up they were all covered in mud, and so we walked up to the drinking tap at the Infirmary and tried to wash the mud off so that we could turn 'em inside out." When I bent down to look at the bundle of mushy paper, Edwin began his tears again and said he was sorry for causing trouble and could he go home. When I told him that we couldn't have supper that night, he started again and I had to buy a stale bun to quiet him. The next day Edwin ran away to his brother, and I found a job charring, on Ordsall Lane."

Such a touching story was Martha's, and for many days after, I felt pangs of sorrow and anguish at her attempt to keep the family intact. Perhaps if I had known the full story of the Cartledge episode at that time…., but then, perhaps it's as well I didn't.

Almost twelve months were to pass before the topic of Edwin Albert Cartledge came to light and only then through a chance remark I had made about the death of his mother in Crumpsall. Kilby's explanation of Edwin's circumstances was made known at the Orphanage on the Saturday when Martha called to take him out for a walk in Broughton Park. Seemingly Martha had pined and suffered in health since losing her brother and had even spent some weeks in the Infirmary as a result of tramping the streets in search of Edwin. When Martha was well enough to earn some money and rent a room she happened to hear that Edwin had asked a street pal to tell her where he was working. Shortly after that conversation and on the very same night, Martha walked from the garrett in Long Millgate to a Casino in Hulme and found her brother working as a skivvy behind the stage. When the relieved Edwin told Martha during their hurried retreat through the alleyways that the older brother would search all Manchest er to find him and take him back, she decided to flee to the haunts of Angel Meadow. At two o'clock in the morning, a 'bobby' from Gould Street found the pair coming out of Sharp Street and, because of the look of distress on their faces, he took them to the All Night Shelter.

Again I cast my mind back to yesterday, and pictured a young Edwin Cartledge who, in an attempt to play the part of the young gentleman, had failed to hold back the childhood tears of a 13 year old teenager in mourning.

Standing next to Edwin at the funeral service was the older and more familiar face of John Raynes, familiar to me because of his long association with the Refuge. If 'Johnnie the elder' — my pet name for him — now number four in my numbering of the 'Manchester Boys', could claim discipleship of the so called 'twelve' then I would have no hesitation in endorsing that opinion. Although Johnnie Raynes was not quite the oldest boy in the group, he was without a doubt the eldest member of the Manchester Refuge Boys, having been rescued when he was only five years of age. Johnnie's great height and physical stature made him stand out as the pinnacle of the group, and his matured looks and easy going composure gave a certain stability to Mr Moody's followers. In my opinion, John was a 'Peter' so to speak, and like the Fisherman of Galilee, a natural leader and a tower of strength.

Spanning the oceans once more, I drifted with time and thought to retrace those early days in Manchester when John Raynes' name first appeared in the register of the Refuge. At that time, there had been a period of hustle and bustle at the Refuge and to make ready for the opening of the very first Orphan Home at 34 Johnson Street, Cheetham. The excitement on the faces of Mr and Mrs Shaw, on that warm sunny day in Peter Street in 1876, was explained to me later as I sat in the offices of the YMCA, writing my monthly newsletter appeal on behalf of the Bible Flower Mission. Leonard Shaw produced an envelope from his jacket and pulled out the significant piece of paper which had culminated in their high spirits. The cheque written and signed by William Atkinson was made payable to the Manchester and Salford Refuges to the amount of £600, the exact amount needed for the outright purchase of the new Orphan Home. Also, I was to learn later, the same William Atkinson, a Southport philantropist, had donated another large sum to Mr Alsop's Wood Street Mission Hall and Ragged School Fund.

I suppose Johnnie Raynes could be referred to as an "Atkinson" Boy, since not only did the Orphan Home adopt the name of its benefactor, but Johnnie was among the first group of children to begin a real home life in a totally new environment.

In a classic example of a 'Deansgate Den', John's story appeared in the local city newspapers a few weeks after he had been taken into the care of the Strangeways Refuges and as a supplement to his background history, the reporter quoted a recently written tract which had been published by Mr Alsop.

"The Saturday night in Deansgate was much as usual. The impudent stare of the shameless — a drunken debauchee — the shivering wife, with starving babe, waiting at the vault door for one who promised to love and cherish — the brutal fight — the policeman's whistle — the fast and gay hastening into ruin, the roar of blasphemy — the subtle thief mixing in with the crowds — the street singer — the lame beggar — the weeping child following a besotted mother — pale parent seeking an erring daughter — the cheap-John's and busy hawkers — the crushing, pushing multitudes amid the blaze of a thousand gaslights. And but a few yards distance, there behind the scenes, flow the floods of sorrow! heaps of misery! and torrents of iniquity!"

According to the City Policy Court, the case of John Raynes went as follows:- "This poor little five or six year old boy was found tied to a bedpost in a garrett in a house off Long Millgate. He had been shamefully ill-used by an uncle with whom he lived, his body covered in bruises." Following the Court drama, the uncle was fined and imprisoned. Winifred Raynes, the sister of this little chap, was accommdated at the Refuge whilst she carried on in service at "The Swan" in Withy Grove. On her signing the usual form, John was admitted to the new Orphan Home whilst Winifred promised to pay two shillings a week towards his clothing. Some years later when reviewing Johnnie's case, Kilby informed me that the sister had since left her employ and was now engaged at Sidebottom's in Portland Street and was living at Bebbington's Boarding House in Angel Meadow. From that meeting with Kilby I was to learn that there were two older brothers, one a soldier and one in the Navy Service.

Johnnie 'the elder', having spent seven years at the orphanage, was known intimately by all the staff at the Refuge, and more as a son by his home mother.

When the decision had to be taken in choosing the twelve boys to follow Mr Moody to Massachusetts, it came as no surprise when John's name was the first ever to be mentioned, for not only had John the ability to succeed, he had always made known his intentions of giving his life to the service of God. I can almost picture the shy awkward look on his face at the time Lord Shaftes bury paid a visit to the Refuge, and John was chosen to present an address to his Lordship. Judging by the way John had taken command of the situation at the funeral, he seemed to be well on his way to achieving his ambition.

THE CHRISTIAN WORKER.

NEWS FROM THE WEST.

OUR engraving represents operations in which our boys in Canada and America have been taking a very active part of late. As the number of our boys across the Atlantic increases, so our correspondence increases year by year; and we are sure that our readers, and all the subscribers to the Strangeways Institution, will be glad to know that those who have been trained under its roof, and have then been placed in homes in the great Western Continent, do not forget " *the old house at home*," or the friends at home to whom they owe so much.

A few extracts from the letters we have received from them will, we doubt not, be interesting; and first we quote from the boys at Northfield :—

"Boys' Home, Mount Hermon.
"I feel very happy here, and I hope I may always keep

so. The place where I live is a Boys' School, where farming and general schooling is taught. It is situated on a mountain, and the scenery all round is very beautiful. We go to the river to practise swimming, and one day I ventured out too far, and should have been drowned had not one of the boys who can swim caught hold of me and brought me to shore. I am thankful to God, who spared my life. Then a few weeks ago I hurt my foot, and it nearly caused lock-jaw, but the danger has passed away. Again have I to thank God that I have been spared. The thought has come over me that, as I had been so near death twice, I was sure that God wanted me for some purpose."

The above is from one of our elder boys. It is extracted from a long letter very beautifully written, and breathing the same thoughtful tone throughout.

Another little man sends a letter to the "Home mother," as follows :—

"Dear Mother,—I now take the pleasure of writing to

'News from the West'.

On a late Spring day in 1879, when the warm genial rays of sunshine filtered through the windows of the Frances Street building, a hand written letter was personally delivered to Leonard Shaw, by a 'Meadow' boy who had previously resided at the Refuge. During a conversation later in the day regarding some charity work taking place in Manchester, Kilby handed me the letter he had received and awaited my comments. Heading the paragraph in bold letters were the words: 'A DAY IN THE COUNTRY FOR THE CHILDREN OF CHARTER STREET AND ANGEL MEADOW'

"Sir,

I would deem it a great favour if you would allow me through the columns of your magazine, to direct the sympathy of your readers to the furtherance of this object.

Knowing something of the homes of hundreds of these children, the privations and sufferings that many of them endure — that Midsummer holidays to them does not mean a holiday, but increased work, in the sale of newspapers, chips, matches etc.

I would be glad if as many as possible would help me to give those little people one good day's enjoyment, making them happy for at least one day of the year, and thus sow seeds of kindness in their hearts, that in the future may bear good fruit, — sending them back to school with many happy remembrances of their holiday. It was my pleasure last year to take 750 children from the Meadow to Worsley for a day, most of them under 12 years of age. I shall never forget the happy faces of the youngsters seated at their midday and evening meals, or their merry laughter as they rolled about in the grass or rose to express their thankfulness. Let us try and cheer the lives of those little ones and I am sure we will enjoy our own holidays the better.

I am Sir,
Yours very respectfully,

Thomas Johnson".
(Charter Street Ragged School)

Recollections of this incident had flirted with my memory only this morning, long before the hot sun had risen above the tree tops and certainly before the service had taken place. Alfred Beasley, one of the Manchester Boys, was busy delivering the fresh milk from the farmstead and his mournful pathetic figure had influenced my thoughts to such a degree that I quickly replaced his sad look with the more familiar one I had known at Cheetham Hill. Alfred's brother, Willie, was the same boy who, according to Kilby, had delivered Tommy Johnson's letter to the Refuge and who would almost certainly have qualified for a place at Mount Hermon, had he not attained his sixteenth birthday and had he not become apprenticed to a Manchester Linen Draper. To my mind, parting the two brothers and dividing the family had seemed a cruel fate, but I was assured that rules were being followed and that this had been the only course open.

The Beasley brothers admission papers to the Manchester Refuges were comparatively uncomplicated and more straightforward than most. Alfred's circumstances, at the time of the so called 'disciple selection' at the Or-

A ragged school outing to Boggart Hole Clough, near Blackley. Drawing by H. E. Tidmarsh.

phanage, had been recorded, as I remember; — "Alfred Beasley, born to a Manchester family on October 3rd, 1872. Father dead, Mother dying, has an older brother named William. The mother has since made a recovery and has obtained light work but is unable to support the boys. She is a respectable and disconcerning woman who has fallen on hard times.

Alfred is a very amiable boy — well disposed, but has not shown yet, much force of character. He has a grandfather, but we have never seen him. He is a popular little fellow at the Cheetham Orphan Homes."

Alfred's popularity, to my mind, was based on his angelic facial expression which was revealed whenever he forced a smile. His wide mouth, a feature which was instantly recognisable, was a hallmark of the Beasleys and, in Alfred's case, emphasised a pronounced cherub-like image. The amiability of Alfred Beasley, a detail which had become so conspicuous at the orphanage had, according to Kilby, contributed to his great popularity on board the 'Cephalonia'.

On the lighter side and remembering how often Kilby had repeated that story, my thoughts turned to the Atlantic crossing and the incident which made Alfred a celebrity on board the ship. Repeating to myself the words which Leonard Shaw had narrated so often:-
"One day, half way between Britain and America, when the waves seemed to lose their height and the seas settled into a heavy calm, a small Manchester boy of about ten years of age volunteered to give a recitation in front of a large gathering of upper deck passengers. Quoting the text from Revelations eleven, twenty five, Alfred nervously began to recite 'The Open Door'. Alfred, like a number of older children at the Orphan Homes, was able to remember the whole of the Manchester 'street waifs' poem which the Rev. Hewlett had donated to the Boys' and Girls' Refuge. With a shy but determined effort, Alfred continued with his rendering of the 'Open Door' —

"You know the Infirmary pavement,
With its broad expanse of stone,
With the Cupola clock overhead, and the
Statues grim and lone,
Crowded and bustling at midday, bright
in the evening's glare,
But on this winter midnight, rain-swept
gloomy and bare.

Twelve from the Cupola clock, twelve
From the clocks all round,
And the lingering boom from Albert Square
With its sad far reaching sound,
Not a soul left in the lonely streets,
all away to shelter and bed,
And the living, throbbing city
seems like a city dead.

Tramp! 'tis the prying policeman,
searching with patient look —

Turning the glare of his lamp,
on each secret corner and nook,
As if on this winter midnight, with the
rain-rush teeming down
Aught, with the life in it,
would stop on the flags and drown.

Ha! what is that then yonder, —
crouched on Wellington's stone?
A lone child, ragged and footbare,
drenched to the very bone.
Grasping the pulpy parcel,
smeared with the roadway mire,
Everything cold about him,
save two little eyes of fire.

"Come!" says the sturdy policeman —
and takes the child by the arm,
"Oh, please don't run me in, sir;
I hasn't done no harm;
'Tis gospel truth as I've told you;
I isn't a prig or a liar!"
"Nay come with me, my laddie,
I'se get thee some food and a fire!"

"Past the hotel over yonder
and just a street before,
There's a place where I'll find thee a lodgin'
it's call 'the open door';
There's a few good folks as keep it
for just such lads as thee —
Look — there it is, right before thee;
go in for thee-sen and see?"

Supper what seems like nectar,
a verse from the Holy Word,
Ten words of a prayer as welcome there
as the grandest litany heard;
a snug little berth and pillow
to rest the weary head,
And God's sweet gift of slumber,
falls on that lowly head.

Oh! type of the door of mercy,
for ever open and free.
Of the dear Lord's word of welcome
the loving "Come unto me."
For even the vilest sinner,
desolate, guilt-stained and poor,
May come to the house of mercy,
and pass through "the open door."

Oh! type of the heavenly city,
that stands in the land of light,
Where pain can never enter,
and the wrong is all set right;
For the gates of that blest city,
are shut not night or day;
And the ransomed people enter
and they that enter, stay."

The passengers, I had been informed, had been moved almost to tears by Alfred's rendering of the poem, and even though Kilby had been on hand to support Alfred through the latter verses, the success had won praise for the entire band of Manchester emigrants.

The thought that the 'twelve' boys from Strangeways had incurred a special preference as to their future, had lingered at the back of my mind on more than one occasion and whilst I supported unanimously the decisions made by Leonard Shaw and upheld the policies of the Refuges in most of its philanthropic endeavours, there was one aspect of this benevolent work which never failed to incite my innermost emotions. On the face of it, 'emigration' in connection with societies such as the Manchester and Salford Refuges was an essential part of the system and, in Leonard Shaw's case, it had become an achievement of which he was justly proud. The 'Manchester to Massachusetts' boys had been acclaimed as a triumph for the institution and a pinnacle of success in its overseas policy of establishing an outpost for Manchester waifs and strays. How I had wished on many occasions that I could imbibe the confidence of those early pioneers who had laid the foundations and given birth to the experimental river of child emigration. Perhaps unfairly and with a misguided conception the movement was incurring, through various publications and rumours, the slanderous labels of 'Child Deportion', 'Child Exploitation', 'Exportation of Child Labour', and 'The Banishment of Waifs and Strays'. Concerned as I was with the progress of the Refuge and perhaps a little more than protective towards Kilby, there was something deeply disturbing over the question of emigration which had caused my own conscience to echo the same anxiety.

How well I remember the article which appeared eighteen months ago, published, as I imagined, to present the Refuges good reasons for using the system of emigration and at the same time dispelling any apprehensiveness.
'From Deansgate to Canada — The Story of John Willie'

"A few months ago in the neighbourhood of Deansgate and the terminus of the Pendleton cars, might be seen every day of the week, and at almost every hour of the day, the subject of these few lines.

He was a regular street child, the gutter his nursery by day and far worse than the gutter, his nursery by night. His father is supposed to have been dead these nine or ten years, and of his mother — how strange and inappropriate the name sounds — the less that is said the better. The mother, when last seen, had added a black eye to add to her other personal characteristics, I think none would be wrong in saying that he had every chance of having his name, sooner or later, added to our long list of criminals.

A kind friend called one Sunday and found the wee chap and his mother at home. After a little talk she promised to bring her boy the next day to the Refuge at Strangeways. However, Monday and Tuesday passed without any news of them, so on Wednesday another visit was paid to the house. The "young hopeful", aware of what was going on around

him, and the mother again the inmate of another institution, begged to be taken away to a better home. What an awful thing for a child of seven years to say of his mother!

On the Saturday of the week following, the leave of his mother having been first obtained, the little lad was taken from Back Clock Alley and sent to the city office in Corporation Street, and in less than two hours had been photographed, washed and fed and was awaiting the time to start for Mrs Birt's Emigration Home in Liverpool, whence he was to sail to Canada.

Leaving the Frances Street Refuge about eight o'clock in the evening, little John Willie trots along by the side of one of his new found friends, to the Central Station. He has boots on his feet certainly, but ne'er a stocking can be seen inside. As trains will not wait for anyone, we have to go pretty fast, but eventually we reach the station with just three minutes to spare. On the way our little hero keeps up a lively rattle with his tongue about the many free rides on tramcars taken, whilst the conductors backs have been turned, and how sometimes he has had a free ride as a reward for assisting in the manipulation of some chain during the turning of a car at the end of its journey.

In the station yard our friend is recognised by an acquaintance, an 'habitue' of the place, who is in an inquisitive mood but is told to be "on his way!" Subsequent questioning as to whom the lad was, elicited the fact that "he is a bad boy; he smokes and swears, and he picks up the ends of the cigars which gentlemen throw away in Peter Street, you know, outside the theatres and those places and smokes them." Thrusting his head out of the carriage window, our little emigrant takes a last long look at the smoke of Manchester and with a final lingering look at the big face of the Central Station clock, sees the end of his old tempestuous past history."

Only recently the editor of the Christian Worker magazine, who had by now captured a young audience in his monthly chapter of emigration, reported the facts of a true story in connection with the work amongst the poor children of the streets.

"Dear Young Friends, — We take up our pen to write to you this month with a somewhat full heart, for we have just taken leave of a party of fifty little boys and girls. This little band of youthful travellers, some of whom we have watched over for years, and love very much, have now sailed for Canada. We are full of hope for this group of children, and I will tell you why we are so, for three reasons:
1st. They are the right sort to go.
2nd. They are going at the right time.
3rd. They are going to the right place.

And what do we mean by saying they are the right sort to go? Well, we mean that there is not a bad boy or girl amongst them! That is a great deal today, is it not? From that band of fifty children who left the Cheetham Orphan Homes on Tuesday last, we carefully excluded those who have shown bad habits or evil tendencies of any kind.

No! the bright and happy homes to which they are go-

Like Dr Barnardo, the Manchester Refuges used the 'before' and 'after' pose in their appeals for charity.

full of hope concerning this little band because they are going at the right time.

And (3rd), they are going to the right place Ah! how important this is. Many a one has lost the battle of life because he has fought it in the wrong place, but these boys and girls are going — To the West! To the West! — to the broad lands of Canada, where there are hundreds of farm houses without a little boy or girl in the family; where there are fathers and mothers with plenty of love to spare for another little one. To the land of plenty, to those happy homes, the children are going. Are we not right, therefore in saying that "they are going to the right place?"

Now, had you seen the little group as they left (accompanied by the good and kind 'Home Mother' to watch over them), you would have seen that each one had a strong square cardboard box, well filled with good and useful clothes; and could you have peeped into those boxes, you would have seen many useful gifts and presents from those who love the children, such as work boxes and Bibles, etc."

These noble words and illustrations had stirred my feelings and no doubt would impress all the kind hearted readers of the 'Christian Worker', but somewhere amongst my personal momentos of the Refuge work, there was one particular reference which I had extracted from the Magazine which I deemed to be of importance. Published at around the time Lord Shaftesbury had been the guest of the Lord Mayor of Manchester in 1883 the article read: "Miss Rye's work among Poor Girls."

"Out of the whole two thousand cases since 1869, there

ing to in 'The land of the West' are too good to be spoiled by sending any but truthful, industrious healthy boys and girls. These are the right sort to go.

But (2nd), they are going at the right time — while they are young, not when they have tried everything else at home, and failed! Not when they are old and broken down in health and spirits. No, that is the worst time to go. But, while they are young and strong, bright and intelligent, and so we are

Every year during the emigration season, children en-route to Canada would stop off at the Manchester Town Hall to be wished a 'bon voyage' by the Lord Mayor and to collect a new shilling.

have not been six instances of ill-usage, and when in 1874 an English inspector of Schools found fault with the system, and a searching investigation was ordered to be made by the Canadian Government, the result was the complete triumph of the emigration scheme, which was proved to be by far the best method yet discovered for converting the raw material of deserted or neglected children — (who in all our large towns, are daily growing up into thieves and beggars, and even worse) — into good and useful members of society, happy honest wives and mothers, as well as excellent customers for English Manufacturers. Miss Rye looks out in every case for healthy country homes for girls, and will do nothing to supply towns people with cheap servants. Most of the children have no-one in England who cares for them, but in cases where this is not so, the children can always be heard of at the 'London Home' or 'Our Western Home' in Niagara."

Way back in 1869, according to my information, when Annie MacPherson had established her Home of Industry at Commercial Street in Spitalfields and, John Barnardo, the medical student, was laying the foundations to his evangelical 'East End Juvenile Mission', another person with the apparent motives of child rescue work entered into the same arena. Maria Susan Rye, a young well-to-do business woman, and reputed to be a missionary amongst the young poor girls of London, had it seemed deserted her former business agency which sent young domestics to the British Colonies, in favour of rescuing little street urchins. Her reasons for conferring her loyalties and entrepreneural expertise on the heads of the little street mites had, it had been claimed, arisen whilst visiting the western states of America, where she had come across the work of Charles Loring Brace, the man from the New York Childrens' Aid Society, whose work amongst the rescued street children had been brought to her attention. Like Annie MacPherson, who had also met Charles Brace in New York, she had been impressed by the successful methods of the Children's Aid Society which had placed thousands of unwanted boys and girls on the farmsteads of the West.

According to the news columns, Maria Rye, with the help from her appeals for money in the Times Newspaper and an influential endorsement from Lord Shaftesbury and the Archbishop of Canterbury, gathered together a total of seventy six little girls and sailed with them on 28th October 1869 to their new western home in Canada. At the onset of the approaching winter, Annie MacPherson, also with the aid of the philanthropic London public, sent her first contingent of families and orphans to Canada.

"Our readers will remember that Miss Rye (whose indefatigable exertions on behalf of pauper children has rendered her name famous) objects to take from workhouse schools grown up girls, but she is willing to accept as suitable for the purpose of emigration, infant children aged about five years."

In a series of articles aimed at influencing the public in favour of emigrating workhouse and destitute children across the Atlantic, the editor of the Liverpool 'Porcupine Weekly', in an edition which coincided with the grand opening of Stanley Park in May 1870, continued his observations thus....

"Miss Rye prefers helpless innocents, whom she is willing to train, — to grown girls badly trained — and she is right."

"Some months ago Miss Rye sailed from the Mersey, taking with her some seventy infant children to Canada West. Fifty of the number were taken from Liverpool Kirkdale Industrial Schools. Well, Miss Rye has written from America, announcing that she has placed successfully in separate homes, every one of these charges, and she has places for at least two hundred more. The project met with great favour in America and she is full of joy and hope for the future. Hear what Miss Rye reports in her admirable let-

A group of new arrivals from England enjoy a momentary pause at the Marchmont Home in Belleville, before their collection by Canadian farmers.

ter recently received from America:

"Our Western Homes, Niagara, Canada, — I, last year, asked for pecuniary assistance to enable me to carry some of our orphan waifs (girls) to Canada and the Western States of America, where I believed I could find good and comfortable homes for many of our perishing and neglected children. I wish now to give an account of my experience, and to tell what has befallen the 70 little ones who, in answer to my appeals were confided to my care last October. My most sanguine expectations have been realised. Every child has a home and there are hundreds of similar good homes offered for many more children as soon as ever I can return to England to fetch them. I am thankful to say that the children from Kirkdale (Liverpool) Industrial Schools where, indeed, I drew my largest numbers, proved capital workers, reflecting the greatest possible credit on the teachers and managers."

Within a month of receiving Maria Rye's letter, the Liverpool News columns were again supporting another appeal on her behalf. This time with a condition that if the Liverpool Select Vestry make an allowance of eight pounds per child, she would be willing to take a further two hundred orphan girls to Canada. As ever, the straightforward arguments portrayed by the Porcupine observed the simplicity of the case:

"The heavy charge of £18 per annum for each child in the Industrial Schools, which must be borne for years, can be avoided by paying down to Miss Rye the £8 per head charge on the grounds of economy. A sum of £1,600 is required by Miss Rye to enable her to take 200 pauper children to America. We earnestly hope that the church wardens will draw upon the voluntary rate for the money."

After an initial experiment at transporting five hundred people (mainly families) to Canada in the Autumn of 1869, Annie MacPherson and her faithful companion, Ellen Agnus Bilborough from Croydon, set sail in May the following year with a party of one hundred boys who had been collected from workhouses and from the London streets. During her visit to Canada, Annie MacPherson founded her new Home in Belleville, Ontario and Ellen Bilborough volunteered to be the matron in charge of the new venture. The house, called 'Marchmont' and provided as a gift by the Belleville townspeople, became inundated by local farmers, all seeking children to employ on their homesteads. This cry for more children prompted Miss MacPherson to telegraph her sister Rachael in London to despatch as soon as possible, a further consignment and, as if literally following in each others footsteps, Maria Rye and Annie MacPherson plied their trade of precious cargo during July, to a country where vast open spaces and clear sunny skies seemed to beckon as the promised land.

According to the Summertime report on Maria Rye's activities, the Liverpool journalist wrote:

"Finding the English people ever responsive to her appeal through the Times, Miss Rye was enabled not only to send a load of children to Canada but also to purchase the 'old gaol' in the town of Niagara which she had now con-

verted into a bright cheerful home. Miss Rye assures us that no limits can be placed upon this work, as the demand for these children is "absolutely unlimited," and she adds, "with God's continued blessing I do not hesitate to say that there is no reason why I should not plant out literally some thousands of our poor little perishing ones."

Mr R N Ball, J.P., writing from Niagara to the editor of the Globe, confirms Miss Rye's opinion, and states "that many shiploads will be required to supply the demand for Ontario alone — and that every child placed out only opens the door for another."

In the melee of child emgiration during 1870, Father James Nugent of Liverpool received commendation for his astute energies on behalf of the Roman Catholic children. "The Reverend James Nugent," so the article read, "stimulated by the energetic action of the indefatigable Miss Rye, has entered the field of emigration and as champion of the scheme, he applied on Tuesday week, to the Industrial Schools for twelve boys and twelve girls to accompany him on his first trip across the Atlantic. With Miss Rye as a friend and benefactor of our Infant Protestant paupers, and Father Nugent as the steadfast and indefatigable friend of the Roman Catholic child, and the unexhaustible resources of our American friends, we may reasonably hope that thousands of our innocent orphan pauper children will be enabled forever to shake off that detestable thing known as the "pauper taint."

By the close of 1871, a year which had seen the bricks and mortar of child emigration undergo a period of stress and a year when Dr Barnardo had, as an experiment, given twelve boys to Annie MacPherson to emigrate to Canada, a concluding passage summed up the feelings of the editorial of the 'Porcupine':

"All honour to Miss Rye, Miss MacPherson and Father Nugent, for their efforts to plant in our distant colonies the poor children from our large towns. They have done well. Miss Rye had made known her intentions of providing homes for a further four hundred children from Liverpool before the winter closes in, and we trust that the public will ignore claims that she is exporting the 'bone and sinew' of England's youth. We know it is said that she will take none but good-looking, healthy girls. She is right. These are the girls who, as paupers, are in most danger in towns like Liverpool. Their poverty and their good looks and associations, make them prey to designing and wicked people.

We notice that Father Nugent's scheme for sending the children to Maryland has attracted the attention of the American Minister; and that in consequence, the Local Government Boards have addressed a letter to the Select Vestry upon the subject. We have already said that Father Nugent should confine his operations to Canada, and we trust that he will henceforth do so."

CHAPTER SIX

Fully fifteen years have now elapsed since Maria Rye and Annie MacPherson began the process of emigration and although the enterprise of those early days carried the blessing of many eminent people, I was still unconvinced of its merits. Even now, with such established emigration homes as Barnardo's, Fegan's, Stephenson's, Annie MacPherson's, Middlemore's, Maria Rye's, Boys' and Girls' Refuges, Mrs Birt's, Catholic Emigration Society, Quarrier's, Children's Aid Society and some others, I could not shake off the suspicion of contriteness. Outwardly, I had been impressed by the calamitous inquiry and verdict of Andrew Doyle, a Dubliner and former Local Government Board official, who had been sent to Canada nearly a decade ago. His findings on Emigration work had not only caused a major controversy in Britain and Canada, but had raised certain questions as to the future policy of sending children abroad, and in such vast numbers. Miss MacPherson's amateur attempts at building her so called 'Golden Bridge' across the Atlantic and her Canadian Homes outpost had, along with Barnardo and Miss Birt, received strong criticism. However, the retired former Poor Law Officer from Plas Dulas in Wales condemned intently the methods and establishment of Maria Rye and concluded that, from her very first shipment of children from Liverpool, she had been motivated by financial gain.

Vividly, I remember Kilby's first public comments on emigration in a paragraph written during the Manchester Society's first term on inauguration.

"We have made an experiment this year in the matter of emigration. Through the kindness of Mr and Mrs Marston, of Kersal, who raised the necessary funds (ten pounds each), the very first (two) Manchester boys have been sent to Canada, under the care of Miss MacPherson. These lads have been with us a few months and had every desire themselves to do well at home, but a wretched mother (a woman known to the police), in the one case, and an unfortunate sister on the other, made it a real blessing to remove the lads from England. They reached Canada in September, and are both now provided with homes, and doing well."

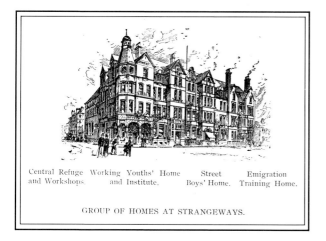

Central Refuge   Working Youths' Home   Street   Emigration
and Workshops.   and Institute.   Boys' Home.   Training Home.

GROUP OF HOMES AT STRANGEWAYS.

Knowing now of the policies of the Refuges, and ever aware of the future commitments of the newly formed Emigration Home, a discerning smile spread across my face when recollecting Kilby's next sentence:

"While we think that any large scheme of emigration for boys would not find public favour, and believing as we do that every boy we are enabled to train up to become an honest and industrious man at home, is so much added to the strength and stability of our country, yet we know that individual cases will arise from time to time (we have one or two in view now) where circumstances are such that emigration becomes almost a necessity, if the boy is to be saved."

A chance remark some years ago prompted Kilby to reveal that Annie MacPherson had written to him from London in 1873 telling him of the progress of the same two boys (the Glynn brothers of Deansgate) and asking for some more boys of the same calibre before the season closes. If perhaps my views on the emigration work displayed a certain ambiguousness, I could only interpret this doubt as a by product of the many letters which I had been privileged to read and which had been written by the Manchester children now in Canada.

Some of those letters scribbled on tiny pieces of notepaper and others on postcards, whilst giving a child's reaction to the resources of the great Canadian outdoors, failed utterly to hide their innocent acquiescence of the vast open prairies and the desolate loneliness of their own beings.

"St Catherines PO
Ontario

Dear Mr Shaw

When we got on the ship and it went into the Atlantic it began to rock and we sicked over each other. We saw a whale and an iceberg and later on we landed in Halifax and we got in to the train waggons and we were three days and three nights and then we landed in Belleville and they were glad to see us. Tonight I am going to a farm. Give my love to Mr Shaw.

P.S. Get as many as you can to come off Angel Meadow as there are many good homes out here".

"Dear Mr Kirlew,

The island where we live is surrounded by the Bay of Quinte and we have the boats running until it freezes in the winter. I am going to school and have to walk four miles a day. I have seen Billy Jones who came out from our Manchester home two years ago. I get up every morning and clean three stables, attend four horses and five cows and milk three of them, then gather the firewood and then get ready for school. But Billy has to clean out four stables, attend eleven horses and twenty-eight cows, milk five of them and then get in the wood and the water and then get ready for school.

P.S. Have you heard from my sister in Manchester, please let me know where she is."

These two letters taken from the top of the emigrant correspondence file were perhaps descriptive of the general flow of letters at the Refuge. Yet, other letters written by the child authors from across the sea revealed certain aspects of their deportation which gave rise to many facets of emigration. Three or four communications within the last twelve months from the Canadian shores, had been of particular interest to me and had incited some unexplained feelings of self condemnation:

"Union Hotel, Selkir, Ontario

Dear Mr Kirlew,
    I have the pleasure in writing to you once more hoping that you are in good health and strength.
    I wrote to you a month or so ago and you did not answer me back again, for I am waiting for the answer that you have found my mother for I have stuck in mind that I would come to England and stay awhile. I think I will come in to you from the summer.'

Yours truly,
Edward Bostick.

P.S. My new address is Commercial Hotel, Garvis, ONT. If you cannot find out my mother any other way give it out at Church time and Sunday School time and if anyone gose to the trouble to find her out I will give them five dollars. Give my regards to Mr Alsop and Mrs Alsop at Wood Street."

"Marple Ridge, Bristol, Canada.

Dear Mr Shaw,
    Again, I am writing to you. Please send me Alice Campbell had-dreass if you please for my sake and if not for my sake, please sent it for God Sake. God forgeve me taken his name in vean, but I cannot help it.
    Write some and let me know how yours all are.

Yours truly,
Peter Campbell."

"Alex Mclean — Farmstead, Thurso, Canada.

Dear Mr Kirlew,
    I like Canada very much. I go to Sunday school and read the bible like you said. I wish there was some more children. Can you send me another boy for a friend, from Mr Alsop's home. I have written to Lord Shaftesbury in England to ask him for my present which was awarded to me by his lordship. Do you remember me and two other boys from Tommy Johnson's Ragged School winning a prize and his lordship writing his name on the front of the book. I forgot to bring it with me. The book was called 'Pilgrim's Progress'. Please Mr Kirlew will you let me know if I have any brothers or sisters or Father or Mother or if I belong to anybody, it gets very lonely out here.

I remain,
Yours truly
Harry Bennett.

P.S. I still remember John 3.16."

Moved as I had been at that time, I was still of the overwhelming opinion that emigration was not the answer to Manchester's problems. As for Miss Rye, her pleas and protestations of victimization had had little sympathy where I was concerned, and in this respect, my Christian principles and sisterly love had been sorely tried. When the facts on emigration had been disclosed in 1875, the country's leading caricaturist George Cruikshank, presented to the nation in newspaper philosophy, his impression of Maria Rye shovelling up scores of little 'gutter-snipes' — her name for street children — from off the streets in front of the Angel public house. Amused as I had been at the illustration as portrayed by the Dickens cartoonist, I rembered thinking at that time and since then, of one particular incident which, had the facts become known, may have influenced the Board of Inquiry and concluded Miss Rye's career in child emigration. Why Maria Rye or anyone else had ignored this vital piece of information remains a mystery to me but, contrary to public knowledge, Miss Rye and her co-worker Miss Smythe — according to a short chapter in a provincial publication — had experimented with a small band of children to Canada prior to the first Liverpool contingent.

"On the exploratory journey," it had been said, "to find and establish a home in the Canadian and American West, Maria Rye together with her Matron Miss Smythe, set sail on the steamship Moravian (Captain Wylie) in mid June 1869, destination Canada. Following the traditional route the ship left Liverpool called at Lough Foyle the following day, and proceeded to Quebec and then Montreal.

On board ship, with Miss Rye were three children whose background was unknown except that they had been inmates of St Pancras Workhouse. The ages of the children, whose future welfare had been entrusted to Miss Rye were five years, ten years and four months respectively."

This seemingly innocent and straightforward transaction by Maria Rye had apparently become obscure and even forgotten, but I was sadly aware and often reminded that the St Pancras baby was only able to survive its first winter, and that by the Canadian springtime, it had lost its hold on life. Of the other two girls, Miss Rye had arranged for their adoption almost as soon as they had arrived in the West.

Perhaps my over-sentimentality towards the children and my over-reactions were obscuring the good results which came about from the Western Home in Niagara and, because of my lack of any qualification on the subject, I would prefer that the last word in this matter should rest with the professional wisdom of Andrew Doyle, who, in his summing up in 1877, wrote:

"I cannot believe that any Board of Guardians in this Kingdom, when informed of the condition and results of Miss Rye's present system, would ask you to sanction the

OUR "GUTTER CHILDREN"

'Our "Gutter Children"' by George Cruikshank

The dialogue is as follows:

Bearded Gentleman with spectacles: There are many plans suggested for providing for the neglected children of Drunken parents, but none such a Sweeping measure as this, for by This plan we provide for them at once, we get rid of the dear little ones altogether.

Lady with chignon: This is a delightful task for we shall never want a supply of these neglected children, whilst the Pious & respectable Distillers and Brewers carry on their trade and we shall always find plenty of the little dears about the Gin Palaces and the Beer shops.

Clergyman: According to the teaching of Jesus, all these little Gutter girls are our sisters, and therefore I feel it my duty as a Christian Minister to assist in this good work.

Lady with Whip (Maria Rye): I am greatly obliged to you Christian ladies and gentlemen for your help and as soon as you have filled the cart I'll drive off to pitch the little dears aboard of a ship and take them thousands of miles away from their native land so that they may never see any of their relations again.

First Child: Mother! Mother! I want my mother! Oh! Mother! Mother!

Second Child: I want my Father!

emigration of another child under it."

Whilst all these aspects of emigration work were recalled to memory, I was reminded of another incident of an unusual nature which occurred at the Wood Street Mission Hall last year. Accepting an invitation to speak on behalf of emigration and to talk about his recent trip across the atlantic, the Rev. R H Lundie of Liverpool explained in an encouraging manner his visit to America.

"It had been," he said "a personal observation of the conditions of our waifs and strays who had been sent to that part of the world. Whilst we were, to some extent, relieving the congested districts of our large towns and rescuing young lives from certain disaster, we were conferring one of the greatest blessings upon the sparsely-populated area of the Far West. I am convinced that this is one of the best remedies for the dreadful street life which so many of our children in Manchester and Liverpool are compelled to live. At a most unusual meeting when I addressed a gathering of American Red Indians, a collection was taken up from those poor Indians and donated to the work of reclaiming street waifs in Liverpool. The amount totalled four shillings and twopence halfpenny."

Another speaker and guest of Alfred Alsop at that meeting was D R Goodwin, who related a very moving story of a little New York street boy who was rescued by a missionary called Charles Brace, and who eventually was given to a farmer. The little boy had not only survived his ordeal but had become a prosperous man, owning 1,000 acres of good land. According to Mr Alsop, this very same man, a devout church attendant and Sunday School preacher, was offering to take 10 strong young lads from the Wood Street Mission to become farmhands in the State of Texas. Although Mr Alsop used the Strangeways Home as a safety valve for the occasional girl or boy whom he thought would benefit from his intervention, the Texas invitation gave the Wood Street Mission its first independent venture into the sphere of emigration, and thus began a journey from Manchester's Deansgate, with the finale on the Mexican border.

Perhaps I should not seek comparisons between the boys who went to Canada and the Moody 'twelve', especially at such a sensitive time as this, and yet there was one very recent letter received at the Refuges which, through the intellect of its author, revealed the inner-most feelings of how one had accepted his emigration:-

"In the first place I remember very little about my poor mother. When she was alive, I was well off, as my father was a dyer. The day my mother died was a sad day for me, but I did not know it at the time. I didn't know I would be begging in Market Street and Peter Street and around Shudehill market place.

I even begged in woollen mills and used to eat stale bread covered in wool. Now I have good Canadian potatoes, and pork and beef, and good home made bread, pies, cakes and puddings and a good roast goose for Christmas.

I often think of those days, and feel like crying when I think of my father and his new wife always fighting and arguing. I'll forgive him now, and may God forgive him. You know there is nothing like a father and mother. Lots of Canadian children have good homes here with real fathers and mothers, and they leave them. I don't know how they can do it; I know I could not if I had a good home like them. Do you remember me coming to your home in Frances Street? I was all rags and dirty and while I sat in the hallway you took my step-mother in another room and that was the last I saw of her.

I left Manchester in 1883, the year Lord Shaftesbury was going to come to the Homes. There were three others, Peter Delaney, Peter Campbell, and the other I forget, only I know he had a white head. We all had velvet suits on and by and by a man came and asked us our names. We went with him to one home and then to another home where there were a lot of Scots boys. To hear them talk was fun to us; they laughed at us. They called our hats, bonnets, and we did not know what they meant by it. After that we all went to Canada.

Your friend, Charlie Connolly."

Leonard Shaw had once tried to explain to me the landscape and scenery of Mr Moody's home at Northfield. "Like the Boys' School it is a home on the hill," Kilby had related, "and set amongst the rolling hills of New England, with sloping meadows which verge towards the wide Connecticut River." With little or no experience in travel pastimes until now, I was unable to judge the comparisons of Leonard Shaw's geographical survey. To my mind, the nearest similarity in landscape features to what now appeared on my horizon, was most likely the familiar view from Alderley Edge and the East Cheshire hills in England, merging with the bordering peaks of Derbyshire. Of course, there was no river valley to speak of, not like the one careering across the broad Connecticut Valley in front of me.

When I return to England, I must make a point of remembering to ask Kilby about the whereabouts of the remaining Platt family in Manchester. My attention had been caught by little Bennie Platt who, before the tragedy, had been the second youngest boy in the school. Now the privilege had become his.

Trotting alongside his brother Fred, the two of them looked like a portrait of desolation as, in a cloud of fretfulness, they carried their loneliness into the pinewoods of Mount Hermon. If ever they needed a mother's hand of sympathy, it was now, I thought, but mothers and fathers were illusionary for most of the boys here.

Benjamin and Frederick Merchant Platt, to give them their full title, had come from an old Manchester family who, at the time of their birth, were living in the village of Denton. Precisely two years ago in August 1882, the Platt family of four brothers and three sisters who were then living in Fairfield Street, near London Road, was devastated by the deaths of their mother and father. Now orphaned in the true sense of the word, the family of brothers and sisters were destined for the beckoning corridors of the workhouse. Fortunately, as I remember the story, two relatives intervened and agreed to take a share of the children's welfare and it was to the grandmother, Mrs E B Merchant, a jeweller by trade, that four of the children were sent.

The next phase in their life is all too familiar, for it was on Christmas Eve day just over eighteen months ago that Fred Platt, together with his little brother, arrived on his eleventh birthday at the Cheetham Hill orphanage. Being Christmas, the two brothers were soon included in the party festivities and, because of the apparent respectability of Mrs Merchant, no scrubbing down or head shaving was necessary. I learned from Leonard Shaw that the two orphans together with their brothers and sisters had lived for a short time with Mr Bullock the milkman, at 87 Fairfield Street and that Mr Bullock, a member of the Fairfield Moravian Church had shown great concern when it was discovered that Mrs Merchant was finding difficulty in making ends meet. In an attempt to stave off the menacing workhouse or industrial school, Mrs Bullock, a friend of the family, suggested to the Rev. Waugh of the Moravians that he might use his influence with the Boys' and Girls' Refuges at Strange ways. Thankfully and happily, I can confirm that the Frances Street committee were more than impressed

when they heard of Bennie and Fred's plight and even suggested to the Grandmother that she could visit or write to them at the George Street orphanage whenever she was able.

When Mrs Merchant called at the offices last year to sign the document which allowed Fred and Bennie to be emigrated to America, she very meticulously handed to Mr Kirlew two little silver lapel pins, one for each boy, telling him that they were mementos which were to be worn on the day of departure. Thankfully, those two family keepsakes, which were still treasured by the brothers as I had observed this morning, reflected not only the bright Massachussetts sunlight, but other glimpses of their previous life in Manchester.

Discounting the present crisis, Fred and Bennie were obviously settling down to their new home and occasionally a letter from one of the brothers to the orphanage had confirmed their contentedness. I often wondered whether they enquired as to the fate of their other brothers and sisters in Manchester, but since they had not mentioned the topic, I accepted that brothers George and Robert and the sisters, Hannah, Mary and Eleann, were content in their own busy lives of industry across the ocean.

Frederick, according to Kilby, was a writer of nice short letters in legible handwriting and was improving all the time. Two of his letters pinned on the office wall at the Refuge had proudly been circulated by Mr Kirlew, the first, dating to October last year:

"Manchester House
Mount Hermon Boys School
Mount Hermon, Mass. USA.

Dear Friends,
I am glad to say we have a chance to write to you, we are all getting on very well on the farm and in the school house. We were digging potatoes yesterday and the day before, I helped with the cows. We expect to go up to the new buildings this month or next. All the furniture has arrived and nearly all the coal. We had some frost this morning and some ice. Miss Jefferson and Miss Freeman are giving us a bible lesson and teaching us letter writing. My school number is 49 and Bennie's is 50. Did you know that 3 more boys came from Liverpool and now there are 15 in our house. There was a big dinner party in Manchester House not long ago and Mr Moody opened all the other houses.

So Goodbye.
Your Friend, Fred Platt."

Fred's other letter to Mr Shaw was a more recent arrival dated only four months ago.

April, 1884

'Dear Mr Shaw,
Our six months ended last Friday. We are all very well here. We English boys will have been here at school one year

next June, and we enjoyed it very well, so far. We had a very good coasting last winter. A good many of the old boys have gone home and their places are being taken by a lot of new boys. We have some new teachers. Mr Hubbard has been poorly and so has Mr Rankin. We have had fine weather lately.

Yours truly,
Fred Platt."

The close relationship between Bennie and Fred had been well illustrated yesterday and I was thankful that today they had each other to lean on. Their attachment to each other had manifested itself on may occasions at the orphanage and they had at times seemed inseparable. One such instance of their togetherness, which will always find a corner in my mind's treasure trove, was the all important day at the Strangeways Refuge when they were enrolled as new members of the Crimson Brigade of the 'Band of Kindness'. On that day a little over fifteen months ago, when preparations were well in hand to stage the 'Donkey and Pet Show'

at the St James' Hall in Oxford Street, little Bennie and Fred arrived at the office of Mr Gilbert Kirlew — known as Uncle Gilbert — to receive their registration numbers, and more important, to put their signatures in 'The Big Book of the Band of Kindness'. This had been a proud moment for the two brothers, especially when the moment had come for the crimson ribbon of the 'B.O.K' to be pinned to their tunics. I can just picture the two Platts as they stood to attention and read together the 'Pledge of the Band of Kindness'.

"I HEREBY PROMISE, by God's assistance, to be kind to all His creatures, to protect them to the utmost of my power; to feed the birds in the wintertime, and never take or destroy a nest. I also promise to show all kindness to domestic animals, and not to take pleasure in hurting them; to be kind to all with whom I may come in contact, and to abstain from all habits that might tend to lower my mind or enfeeble my health. I will also endeavour to get as many boys and girls as possible to join the Band of Kindness."

The Piccadilly Infirmary with its cupola clock and pavement statues. Courtesy: Chris Makepeace.

Absorbed as I had been with Bennie and Fred Platts' circumstances another little fellow and a pal of Ben's was vividly brought to mind as I looked down from my vantage point in the direction of the Manchester cottage. Was it only three, or was it four years ago when young Walter Walker first made his appearance at the Refuge? This question caused me to reflect more clearly over which day I was trying to pinpoint. The only clue I could think of was that it must have been some time between the Whitweek parades through Manchester and — yes! it was clearer now. The year was 1881 and Mr Shaw had called a special meeting of city charity workers to discuss the forthcoming Christian Conference.

Arriving early on that day, I was ushered by Mrs Browne through the reception room where a small group of ragged boys were sat, and from there into the adjacent committee room. Trying hard not to ask the questions which were on the tip of my tongue, in regard to the sight I had just witnessed, I focused my attentions on the decorative wall artistry and the many tracts of bible philosophy. Amongst the more familiar mottos were two which never failed to attract my outright attention and once again I read aloud the wise words of William Chambers:-

"God's Plan for Bringing Up Children —

The family system is the foundation of everything that is valuable in our institutions. Our whole structure of society rests on it. Any attempt to rear children artifically on a wholesale principle is necessarily defective, will prove abortive, and be attended, one way or another, with bad effects."

"HE SETTETH THE SOLITARY IN FAMILIES."

Exhibited next to the Chambers philosophy was an equally moving testament and one of my own favourites;
    "What more can a child want?
    Only one thing; but that one thing is everything to a child; it is love, that mother-love for which all children long, for which the childish heart yearns and which is the great moulding power in a child's life. This is wanted."
    Trying hard to catch another glimpse of the little urchins, I edged nearer to the window pane by the connecting door and, in so doing, came face to face with a recent addition to the poetic gallery of quotations. In very large print on the door panel the text:-"And Cry of the Children", stood out like 'Big Abel' in Albert Square. With the instant recognition of my favourite poem I pursued the reason for it, until discovering that this title had been adopted as the new motto of the Boys' and Girls' Refuges and also as the title for the new magazine to be published by the society. Time, or the surplus of time, was still in my favour as I sat in the waiting reception sipping my hot tea and almost unthinkingly I focused my mind on the "Cry of the Children", the words of which making pleasant vibrations as they filtered from memory to mind. Gradually the verses became exposed, and though incomplete, created the stimulus for an oratorical expression.......

Children 'on tramp' take refuge at the Stockport Ragged Schools. Circa 1865. By kind permission of Stockport library, who donated these photos from their 'Ragged Schools' collection.

London 'Street Waifs'. Circa 1900. By kind permission of the NSPCC.

"Do you hear the children weeping, Oh my brothers,
Ere the sorrow come with years?
They are leaning their young heads against their
mothers,
And that cannot stop their tears.
The young lambs are bleating in the meadows,
The young birds are chirping in the nest,
The young fawns are playing with the shadows,
The young flowers are blowing towards the West —
But the young, young children, O my brothers,
They are weeping bitterly!
They are weeping in the playtime of the others,
In the country of the free.

They look up with their pale and sunken faces,
And their looks are sad to see,
For the man's hoary anguish draws and presses,
Down the cheeks of infancy.
'Your old earth', they say 'is very dreary,
Our young feet; they say, 'are very weak!
Few paces have we taken, yet are weary —
Our grave — rest is far to seek'.

Alas, Alas, the children! they are seeking
Death in life, as best to have;
They are binding up their heart away from breaking,
With a cerement from the grave.'
Go out, children, from the mine, and from the city,
Sing out, little children, as the little thrushes do;
Pluck your handfuls of the meadow cowslips pretty,
Laugh aloud to feel your fingers, let them through!

'For Oh', say the children 'we are weary,
And we cannot leap,
If we cared for any meadows, it were mearly
To drop down in them and sleep.
Our knees tremble sorely in the stooping,
We fall upon our faces, trying to go;
And underneath our heavy eyelids drooping,
The reddest flower would look as pale as snow.

And well may the children weep before you!
They are weary ere they run;
They have never seen the sunshine or the glory
Which is brighter than the sun.
They look up with their pale and sunken faces
And their look is dread to see,
For they mind you of Angels in high places
With eyes turned on Deity!"

Reflecting on the Strangeways home and its staff on the other side of the Atlantic, I concluded that Walter Thurlow Browne, the kind hearted and long serving master of the Refuges, would by now, be wearing the impressive cap and gown of his new appointment at Cheetham's Public School. His recent move to Manchester's famous seat of learning had caused many sad faces at the Strangeways Home and not least to those boys whose memories stretched back to their first foothold at the rescue society's headquarters. One such boy was Walter Walker, one of the youngest boys now at Mount Hermon School. His memory of Walter T Browne would probably be that of a kindly faced master who had not only shown him some affection but who through his personal endeavours had given him a new hope and a new life.

Unknown to me at the time, Walter Walker was one of those street children who in his tattered state and forsaken looks had stood out amongst the others and who had captivated my attention on the day of that special meeting. Mr Browne's devotion to his welfare work amongst the street boys of Angel Meadow was well known at the Refuges, but what surprised me was the great compassion he had portrayed in a very touching story which he had composed about the Walter Walker incident. Speaking to his audience through the monthly magazine, a tale I clearly remember, he went on; —

"The cry of the children, yes reader, of little children — of perishing children — has been reaching our ears and our hearts in a very special manner of late. Little fatherless and motherless ones, with nothing before them but the workhouse or the street, have been stretching out their hands for help, and at times we have felt almost powerless to aid; for the cries were so many, and our means of helping them so small. We shall tell you reader; of just one of those cries, which has come to us during the past month — from the neglected courts of Angel Meadow. His appearance as he sat in the ante-room at the Refuge comes vividly to mind. Long matted locks, pale pinched face, bright eyes full of intelligence, and a quickness of manner indicative of a precosity of mind. We noted that his entire wardrobe consisted of a ragged shirt, a piece of string for a brace, and an old pair of trousers requiring an inspection to identify them. Our hearts' best sympathies went out towards this poor mass of wretchedness. Again flits before the memory the prayer that the Refuge might be a blessing to the newcomer:-

"We thank thee for the lesson, Lord,
Thy miracles have taught,
For thou didst bless and multiply
The little that was brought.'

And so we bring with deepened faith
The 'fragments' of our street,
We gather up the 'broken' ones
And lead them to thy feet."

To look at the poor little mite, his drawn, wan face not only tells of want of food, but it also bears the marks of cruel usage. Fatherless and motherless, he had been left at an early age to the tender mercies of an older relative in wicked surroundings.

Those ears and eyes, so quick to learn at his age (8 or 9 years), are accustomed to oaths and curses, and fighting and misery; what wonder if the little fellow, set out ragged, dirty and half-starved to school, should wander now and

Boys from the poorer areas of Manchester and Salford are seen here at Wood Street Mission, all hoping to obtain a 'pass' for a holiday outing.

then to a kind neighbour. It was this neighbour, dear readers, who showed him some of that motherly love for which his little heart longed, and it was she who sheltered the poor little object when she found him sleeping in a coal yard, covered by a few odd pieces of garment.

"It would be a real charity to take him in, gentlemen, for he is shamefully used."

Yes, his very appearance is an unspoken "cry" which we cannot resist. We have just one vacancy in our Orphan Homes, and so we decided to take him there. Our kind Mr Shaw now seeks a pair of shoes to cover the naked feet, ere we take him up; but alas! the poor little feet are so bruised and blistered that he cannot bear anything on, and so he trots along by our side, barefoot, to Cheetham Village, and soon the little weary one is at rest in his new home."

When I once commented on Walter's unfortunate circumstances, Kilby confided that there were three older brothers whose names were Edward, Fred and Jonathon, and when the parents were alive they had all lived at a house in Ellor Street, Pendleton. What I found so distressing about little Walter was Kilby's concluding remark on the subject: "This fellow was found living with the older brother Edward in great neglect and destitution. Not only was he covered in sores, his little back was so painfully bruised he was unable to wear a shirt for some days after his rescue."

To my way of thinking, the modest Leonard Shaw had scored a personal triumph in connection with the great Christian Conference which he and the Refuge committee had organised in 1881. The Manchester headlines summed up the approaching important occasion of the three day conference in October as a "stirring up of God's people." "Our readers will be glad to learn," went the article, "that the arrangements for this important gathering of the Kingdom's leading workers amongst 'Orphan and Destitute Children' are in active progress."

Overwhelmed as I had been at meeting all the leading campaigners of child rescue work, and enlightened by so much knowledge during the hours of speech making, I still regarded those few days of the Great Conference as one of the milestones of my life. Beginning with the Conference Sunday on the 23rd, the main hall at the Refuge was packed as I had never seen it before. All the children from the Orphan Homes were there, as were the boys and girls from all the other branch homes of the society including the Strangeways Home. Boys from the Shoe Black Brigade and Parcel Brigade, girls from the Girls' Working Home and the Emigration Training Home, more boys from the Working Boys' Home and young sailors from the Training Ship 'Indefatigable' at Liverpool. Some young ones and the Matron had come from the Night and Day Shelter in the City and another group of people had travelled from the Southport Summer Camp.

Addressing the masses of people that afternoon, Mrs Louise Birt (Annie MacPherson's youngest sister), of the Liverpool Sheltering Homes for Orphan and Destitute Children, gave a very enlightening account of her work amongst the waifs and strays of Liverpool and of her emigration work to Nova Scotia and the Colonies. Sharing the stage with Mrs Birt was an old friend of the Manchester Refuges who was more familiarly known as David Harris of Edinburgh. His beautiful rendering of 'The Good Samaritan' had made an impression on even the youngest of the audience but it was perhaps Mrs Birt's true account of an incident which had taken place in Canada that captured the imagination of the majority of the children. Speaking in her strong Scot's accent and simplifying the story in its detail, she related how, some years earlier, two young boys had been found in a graveyard in Vauxhall Road, Liverpool, and were sent to the Workhouse whilst inquiries were made into their circumstances.

"After a few weeks the friendly magistrate gave permission for the two boys to be taken care of at our Sheltering Homes and they remained with us for about six weeks. A few days before they were due to sail for Canada, a father of Dick Kearns (one of the boys) came and claimed him.

The other boy, Harry Taylor, being an orphan, was unclaimed and was eventually placed in a good farm home.

An appeal from the Boys' and Girls' Refuges, Manchester.

Some two years after this, an old woman called at our Home and begged us to take an orphan girl in, who, she said, she could no longer afford to keep. In departing she remarked that there used to be a brother but he had disappeared. We took the girl in and after a period of training she was taken to Canada and settled in a house near to where the boy Taylor had been placed. Imagine our pleasant surpise when some time later it was found Harry Taylor's new English neighbour turned out to be his very own sister from Liverpool."

On Monday the 24th, the Conference opened with a united prayer meeting in the 'Moody Hall' of the YMCA, in Peter Street, and later in the afternoon a 'Welcome' meeting took place at the Lecture Hall of the Strangeways Refuges. Heading the first meeting of the seminar under the title: 'The Tower of Faith and Prayer amongst Destitute

Poets' Corner on Long Millgate Manchester, opposite Cheetham's College entrance. Drawing: H. E. Tidmarsh.

Children", Miss Mittendorf of Surrey began the proceedings and was followed by Miss Sharman and Mr Clifford of London. At six o'clock that evening, after a visit to the Strangeways Branch Homes and the Cheetham Orphanage, the special guests of honour sat down to a tea at the Refuge before preparing for the evening public conference at the YMCA.

It is difficult to say which speech or which speaker impressed me the most during the conference but, amongst all the eminent orators and the high-ranking dignitaries, my attention was captivated by the genteel statuette character of little Ellice Hopkins of Brighton. In the shadows of such powerful renderings delivered by her stage colleagues, Miss Hopkins gave an address on rescue work, especially amongst little girls, a subject in which she was intimately knowledgeable. Quoting from her own writings and referring to the experiences of her friend Dr. Barnardo, she stilled her audience with a combination of intellectual oratory and quiet but powerful deliverance. My endeavour to seek out Ellice Hopkins at the close of the evening session was rewarded with an introduction and handshake with some of the guest speakers, amongst whom was the monocled Dr Barnardo, Canon Bardsley, the Rev Wilberforce Starr, Rev T B Stephenson and the Bishop of Manchester. Miss Hopkins had been engaged in a lengthy conversation with her close friend and famous Manchester philanthropist Frank Crossley for most of the retirement period, but during my brief interlude a reference was made to Mr Moody of America and his new Boys' School.

The second Conference Day in Manchester turned out to be one of the most eventful days in the history of the Boys' and Girls' Refuges, and one which brought a ray of sunshine to the disconsolate habitats of Angel Meadow. Following another day of important speeches the reverent and honoured guests, after a lunch at the Refuges, made their way in small groups along Old Millgate and arrived in good time for what had been officially advertised as "The Opening of the 'Old Victory' — Boys' Rest, Lodging House and Coffee Tavern, Charter Street, Angel Meadow." In declaring the 'Boys' Rest' to be "well and truly opened", and after paying tribute to Mr Shaw, R B Taylor and Mr Kirlew, Dr Barnardo made a particular reference to the other 'old Victory', the Edinburgh Castle in his own East End of London, a similar one time Gin Palace, now converted to refuge and rescue.

When the finale to the third and final day of the Conference did arrive, it took place at St Ann's Church at a special evening Communion service for all the participants of the convention. As Kilby wrote later in his summing up of the event:-
"About eighty members of the Conference, gathered from almost every section of the Christian Church, met at St Ann's — the Church where in olden times John Wesley had preached, and where in later years the same gospel had been proclaimed with no less earnestness by the Rev. Canon McGrath, Rev. John Richardson and the Rev. Canon Bardsley."

I had been warned that Wednesday would be the busiest day of the Conference, a remark which turned out to be an understatement in view of all the meetings and speakers I had written into my agenda. Firstly, a discussion on 'Emigration' had taken place with the meeting being chaired by the Prebendary MacDonald, Rev. Dr. Pope and Rev. J A MacFadyen. The main speakers at this session were: Annie MacPherson, William Quarrier, Dr Barnardo, Louise Birt, Alfred Mager and Alfred Alsop. During the afternoon's 'Give and Take' conference a selection of subjects chosen for discussion were 'Juvenile Street Hawking', 'Family Homes', 'Boarding Out System', 'State Labour Schools', 'Training Ships', 'Homes for Crippled Children', the response to questions and answers being given by Sam Smith, J P of Liverpool, the Hon Arthur Kinnaird of the YMCA movement and Leonard Shaw.

Speaking on the subject 'Children for Christ', the concluding meeting of the Conference brought an inspirational speech delivered by the Rev T B Stephenson of the London Children's Homes and the theme, which had been thought appropriate to end the Manchester Conference, was well received at the packed Association Hall of the YMCA. Before his audience and a notable panel of supporting speakers which included Barnardo, Canon Stowell, F N Charrington and J W C Fegan, Mr Stephenson went on to say that he had often come across scenes depicting Christ blessing the Children, as referred to by Prebendary MacDonald. What he had not seen was anything that embodies his own idea of what actually took place. The children in the pictures he had seen were represented as very clean looking, well dressed and cherub like darlings. Surely if it was the common people who 'heard him gladly' we may very properly assume that it would be the 'poor children' or the 'street children' of Jerusalem that were brought to the Saviour. It was these little ones that reminded Him of His Father's house, for He said, "Of such is the Kingdom of Heaven."

In a manner of speaking, it was those last few words quoted by Thomas Stephenson which literally brought my thoughts back to the Northfield setting and more appropriately to the fate of the deceased boys. If theirs was the Kingdom of Heaven, I thought, gazing at the peaceful serenity of the surrounding acres, then they must now dwell amongst the celestial gardens of Mount Hermon.

There was another reason for reminding myself of Thomas Stephenson. His was one of the names which appeared in a newsletter written by Mr Kirlew of the YMCA in Manchester and later published by the Manchester Guardian. A copy of that article intended for Mr Moody was in my possession at this very moment. Perhaps this was not the time or the place to read Mr Kirlew's 'American' letter of last year, but I decided to face the subject now rather than bring it up later. Beginning with a geographical account of his journey Mr Kirlew went on:

"I have visited many places in Canada, and in the following state of the Union: Wisconsin, Minnesota, Nebraska, Dakota, Iowa, Illinois, Michigan, Indiana, Maryland, Virginia and all the New England States. In all these, but especially in the Western States and Western Canada, the demand for males and females willing to work is exhaustless. Bishop Welles of the Episcopal Church of Winsconsin told me it would confer the greatest possible boon on his country and ours to encourage such people to emigrate to the West, and hundreds of people of all denominations and of different social positions, in all parts of the country, re-echoed his opinion. Even for child labour the demand from farmers is enormous. I had the pleasure of visiting the beautifully kept reception home, near Hamilton, Ontario, in connection with the Rev. T B Stephenson's Homes at London and Bolton, England, for reclaiming street urchins. I spoke there to about 40 lads who had arrived from England the previous week, already sunburnt and happy, and the manager told me he had had letters from farmers for ten times the number.

I saw on Mr D L Moody's farm at Northfield, Massachusetts, the boys taken there by Mr and Mrs L K Shaw of the Manchester and Salford Street Childrens' Refuges. The boys were busy making hay. Most of them know me by my going to the Refuges in Strangeways and when I asked them if they would like to return with me, they grinned all over their happy looking sunburnt faces and said, "No, Sir, thank you, we would much rather be here." When I was in Montreal, Mrs Birt of the Sheltering Homes, Liverpool, brought to her Canadian Receiving Home, Knowlton, Near Montreal, fifty female children, and in one week had inquiries from farmers for four hundred and fifty."

Mr Kirlew's serialisation of his American journey was published in two parts and as an active participant at the

The Rev. T. B. Stephenson of the Children's Home with some of the children he cared for. By kind permission of the National Children's Home.

Refuges I felt compelled to read again the second and more topical observation which he had captioned:-
"Mr Moody at Home — The Manchester Street Lads."

"Today I visited Mr Moody's farm at Northfield. The situation is lovely, on the slopes of hills on both sides of the River Connecticut, which can be seen from a long distance gliding through a beautiful valley surrounded by the tree covered hills of Massachusetts, New Hampshire and Vermont, which three States have their juncture near to Mr Moody's house. This morning, after breakfast and family worship, he drove me to the house — a little higher up the hill, behind his house — where he was born, and introduced me to his mother, who has lived as a widow there for forty two years; thence to the Seminary nearby, a handsome brick building which he has erected so that about fifty young ladies from different parts of the country may there receive a thoroughly Christian educational and domestic training, to fit them for taking charge of schools. When one thinks of the influence these ladies, thus qualified, will exert on many of the rising generation, it is impossible to estimate the good they do. One of the students, a Canadian, asked me if there was any truth in the statement someone had made to her that Queen Victoria was about to abdicate in favour of the Prince of Wales, and was immensely relieved when I told her it was untrue and that someone had been chaffing her. From thence we drove through the one long tree-lined street of Northfield, its churches and houses made of wood, white painted, green shuttered, like all American villages. The two churches of Northfield are Unitarian and Congregational; in the former, Mr Moody's father worshipped when alive, and in the latter, Mr Moody does when at home.

From thence, we drove down the hill on to the ferry boat worked by a wire rope, so crossed the river and drove up the hill on the opposite side to the five cottage homes prepared for boys. The first one was named last week by Mr Dan Boyd 'The Manchester Home', because in it are boarded the twelve Manchester Boys who were brought here a fortnight ago by Mr and Mrs Shaw. It is in charge of two Nova Scotians, gentle and refined, who have been trained in the Seminary. The boys were busy making hay after having milked the cows, and seemed thoroughly happy.

Mr Moody told the boys he had brought a great quantity of fireworks from Boston to help tomorrow's celebration (the fourth of July) and they evidently looked forward to having a big time; but when the boys were asked to give three cheers for Independence, the Manchester Boys, true to Queen and Country, remained silent.

In one of these homes there are two lads, brothers, whose story is a touching one. Their father was a London Barrister whose circumstances became very reduced, and he died leaving his family very destitute. His widow died soon after in Liverpool, her death-bed greatly saddened by fears of what would become of the children when left orphans. One, a girl, was taken by a friend and, when Mr Moody was holding his mission in Liverpool, he heard of the case and at once said he would take the two lads into his school at Mount Hermon. Here they are now, happy and, contented and having been well trained at home, are exercising a good influence on the other inmates of the home.

Although it was eleven o'clock at night when we drove up to Mr Moody's door, he announced our arrival by blowing a big horn, almost as big as himself, to the intense amusement of his children and some of the young people from the Seminary, and only desisted when Mrs Moody reminded him he would waken the neighbours. This horn was one of the many things he had brought with him from Boston to make fun for the girls and boys on Independence Day. I confess to a kindlier feeling for a man who cannot only sway the masses and control a great gathering, but who also has a practical sympathy with young people at school and at play.

In going with Mr Moody to the Female Seminary and the Boys' School, I was struck with the variety and aptness of his questions, and the apparent perfect concord between him and the students. In the Female Seminary during the past year, there have been 51 boarders, including five from Canada, one from Germany, one from Bulgaria and ten Indian girls, belonging to the Shawnee, Cherokee, Creek and Chocktaw nations. The students perform the work in the house under the supervision of the Matron. There is a good chemical laboratory for practical work, and the philosophical room is well supplied with valuable apparatus. The girls also have a Missionary Society, which meets monthly, and its proceeds are given to the education of a girl in Miss Mumford's school at Philipopolis, Bulgaria.

The Girl's seminary is shared by 101 day pupils from Northfield and surrounding districts, who each pay £4.5shgs per annum. The boarders, who must be at least 15 years old, must have a certificate of good health and be required to pass exams in Arithmetic, Geography and grammar. When accepted, they must be able to pay £20. per annum for tuition, board and lodging. The lady principal, who recently married the minister of Northfield Church, is an M.D., and there are five other teachers, three assistants and two matrons.

When we visited the Boys' School, Mr Moody showed by his questions and answers that he was equally at home with the boys in school and at play. The way he called attention to an injured cow, and the tear which came to his eye as he spoke to me about the barrister's sons above referred to, revealed to me some tenderness under that apparent brusqueness of manner to which all we who had to do with him in England got accustomed. Then his jokes with the boys about the fun he was providing for Independence Day, and his lively invitations to the farmers we met to join therein, showed another side of his character which I can appreciate.

Whether I adopted a sideways glance or a head on stare at the Manchester House, there was no escaping the heaviness which hung like a stage curtain waiting to draw its drapes around the setting. As an outsider and a visitor to Mount Hermon, I could easily have chosen the role of the sympathetic friend or the kindly Aunt. Instead I was confronted with ten individuals whose only desire was a mother's shoulder where emotions could find a release. Knowing intimately the past history of all the English boys, I really didn't have any such choice. Their sorrow was my sorrow and their mourning had drawn me into the close brotherhood of the Manchester family. Losing a close friend or a loved one was an experience not unfamiliar to the boys from the Refuges, a fact which manifested itself amongst most of the children at Strangeways, and probably more so in the case of John Caton's pal.

George Woodhouse, now aged 14 years, was a boy who had witnessed the loss of four close friends, each of them having been the victims of drowning. Discounting the Connecticut incident, George Woodhouse was a young boy who not only had to cope with the present event, but was almost certainly reliving the painful experience which had occurred in Manchester four years earlier, and was the very reason for his presence in Massachusetts. I am not sure about the facts and figures surrounding George's early life in Salford but I do distinctly remember Kilby showing me a newspaper cutting in connection with the tragic loss of his mother when he was just ten years old.

"A poor striving woman, living in Gravesend Court, Salford, of whom little was known beyond the fact that she worked at a Manchester mill and was found in the canal the previous Saturday morning, life extinct." Continuing the details of the inquest, the report went on:-

"It was proved that she had left work at the usual time the previous evening; but whether owing to the fog which prevailed, she had accidently walked into the canal, or, borne down by the weary load of life, she had deliberately ended her life there, will never be known."

"She was young; she was fair. She had left two little boys behind her, for whom she toiled hard. No motive could be assigned for the deed, and so the jury returned the usual — the only verdict possible — 'Found Drowned'."

I suddenly remembered my reaction at the time of this tragedy and how I wished she — the mother — had chosen the daylight hours for the purpose in mind. At least there would have been a chance of a Mark Addy in the Vicinity coming to her rescue.

On the death of the mother, William Frederick, the older of the two brothers, was taken by an Aunt known as Nurse Taylor of Bank House and whose residence was situated at 'The Cliff' in Seedley. When, according to Leonard Shaw, little George had been claimed by Mr and Mrs Browning, the elderly neighbours of Gravesend Court, the chapter of events appeared to have found a happy ending. However, the story of George Woodhouse, a tale which is now familiar to all the workers of the Refuges, was given a new lease of life about two years ago.

As the Strangeways committee so proudly boasted in their monthly magazine at that time, "Few things are more encouraging as we toil at night and day amongst the street boys of our city than to hear of a rescued one who has gone forth from our Refuge to fight the battle of life alone, doing some brave and noble deed. Such a genuine pleasure was ours as we read the following account as published by the Royal Humane Society.

"On March 13th, 1882, Edmund Joules, able seaman of Her Majesty's ship 'Valiant', jumped overboard in the Irish Channel, a heavy sea running, to the rescue of William O'Connor, but Joules, having a broken arm and a sling, was unable to hold the man up without some assistance. Two other men then jumped overboard and assisted Joules to hold the man above water until a boat was sent. Edmund Joules was awarded the Bronze Medal of the Royal Humane Society, and Testimonials were voted to the other two seamen."

When it became known at the Refuges that the Duke of Edinburgh had personally awarded the medal to Edmund Joules and that Lord Brassey, a Lord of the Admiralty, had presented special prizes to three other Manchester Refuge boys, who were serving on the training ship 'Indefatigable', a great feeling of proud achievement seemed to engulf the society.

"Indeed," as Kilby explained some time later, "the whole of Manchester and Salford seemed suddenly aware of what our aims were and of our mission amongst street children in the alleys."

As a direct result of the "Sailor Boy's" story which was published in the Christian Worker, an old couple living in Bridge Street on the Salford side of the Irwell, decided that if Edmund Joules, a "rough diamond" of a boy, who once terrorised them at the Wood Street Mission, could end up like the hero he had, then there was a place on the Training Ship for their boy. That evening Mr and Mrs Browning arrived at the Frances Street Refuge with "their" boy whom they wanted to enlist as a 'sailor boy'. During the conversation, the realization that the young lad that was being deposited, named George Woodhouse, was the same one that had been orphaned by the drowning of the mother two years previous, suddenly dawned on Kilby. Even the verse he had quoted at that time surfaced for a few moments enabling him to echo the same words,
"One more unfortunate, weary of breath, —
claimed by the Irwell, and gone to her death."

The next day, after several discreet enquiries, Leonard Shaw came to terms with what he called a very touching tale regarding George Woodhouse. "It was apparent", Kilby explained, "that Mr and Mrs Browning were most genuine in their concern for the lad, believing that a navy career would be the answer, both for the immediate and long term future prospects. What was so painfully obvious and what the old couple were too proud to admit was the fact that their kind deed in providing a home for George had by now taken a toll of what little savings they had put by. The dreaded 'house' test was staring them in the face and every week's refuge afforded to George was merely a deposit on their own future lodgings in the workhouse." As usual, and with his endless supply of sympathy in matters concerning children, Kilby accepted George Woodhouse that very same day and, along with his committee, recommended the boy's instant removal to the Cheetham Hill orphanage.

At the hillside ceremony this morning, George Woodhouse had stood tall and silent, his tanned rugged farmboy features giving no indication of his innermost feelings. To me, this former Manchester orphan would always be the "seed in the city wall", a quotation which again I have to thank Kilby for. As in so many of Kilby's jottings and scribbled notes, conclusions to case histories, especially if deemed to be successful, more often than not, qualified for a form of poetic contribution. Seemingly, Kilby had shown a great deal of concern over Mr and Mrs Browning, almost as much as for young George, and he arranged for the couple to call and see the boy once a week at the orphan home. His regard for the dead mother, the future of George, and the elderly foster parents, was amply evident in the summing up of the 'Woodhouse' case, a chapter brought to an end with the now familiar verse:

"Only a seed, — but it chanced to fall
In a little cleft of a city wall;
And taking root, grew bravely up
Till a tiny blossom crowned its top.

Only a thought, — (the Brownings) — but the work it wrought,
Could never by pen or tongue be taught,
For it ran through a life like a thread of gold
And the life bore fruit a hundred fold."

George appeared to have withstood the emotional drama of yesterday even to the point of taking on the parental guardian attitude where the other boys were concerned. To some degree I admired his stand and protective instincts but somehow I could not help but feel his brave actions were just a cover for his own turbulence and emotional conflicts. Although George was still a good deal taller than his room mates, his ability to look the senior boy in the group had diminished, partly due to the maturity of the most high ranking of the Manchester 'twelve'.

Known as the 'professor', Frank Linley Critchlow, now 16 years of age, was once described by Leonard Shaw as being: "an amiable and sensitive lad of great ability but not perhaps, so energetic as others." Frank Critchlow had proved his 'ability' during his first twelve months at Mount Hermon and his outstanding academic achievements had been a source of inspiration to the Manchester boys.

Kilby had made no secret of his feelings towards Frank Critchlow and of the high hopes for his future life in America. As a pupil of St John's School in Cheetham, Frank had attained an excellent report from his master who had convinced Leonard Shaw that his chances for the future would benefit from his emigration to Mr Moody's school in

Massachusetts at Mount Hermon.

Through Kilby and having met and talked with Frank at various functions connected with the Refuges, I came to know a young man who not only seemed to know just where he was going in life, but how he intended getting there. His letters to the Manchester Homes had not only become more frequent but were now looked upon as the best source of information from across the Atlantic. Whenever an incident took place in connection with the school or if Frank felt an inclination to develop his poetic tendencies, his lengthy communications would always cause Kilby to heave a sigh and utter his appreciation. Then as always, he would make a point of making sure that everyone at the institution had a chance of reading the latest adventures of the Manchester 'twelve'. Just a few weeks before I left the Strangeways home for my present destination, Kilby had proudly shown me that latest news from Mount Hermon. In sentences which were more akin to poetry, Frank Critchlow had gone into flowing detail regarding the Mount Hermon boys' attempts to landscape the rough terrain outside the new cottages. "Assisting Mr George Moody", (Dwight Moody's brother) he had said,

"We Hermon boys the land made bare,
then hoed and toiled till grass grew there.
Along muddy paths where trees were few,
we planted elms until they grew."

Those same elms were now in view as I turned my head in the direction of the path leading downhill towards the Connecticut River. Standing at about ten feet, I could imagine how they would look in years to come; a beautiful tree lined avenue where the leaves and branches of the great elms would cast their cooling shadows on a hot summer. The grass shoots Frank had referred to were at this moment fields of harvest gold, but I have no doubt that the sloping hills of springtime would have been bathed in emerald green.

Being the eldest of the 'twelve', Frank Critchlow had incurred a responsibility and a leadership which served to make him appear older than his sixteen years. His authority and guidance at today's service were an inspiration to the rest of the Manchester boys, and although the emotions had given way at times, he had retained his hold of the situation. In a kind of tutorial manner there were prominent signs of superintendancy about Frank Critchlow, a fact which Kilby had mentioned on more than one occasion. In particular, there had been an incident at Charter Street Sunday School when Frank, along with some of the older boys from Strangeways, had been asked to help with a teaching session. In illustrating his interpretation of the English language, young Critchlow had very cleverly involved his young audience in expressing in verse a description of their existence on the streets of Manchester. With a simple but effective method of communication and with a little help from the ragamuffin children, Frank Critchlow's efforts on the board and easel developed into a short condensed piece of poetry which not only pleased the children, but came to be

Chapter Eight

acknowledged by Mr Browne as "a fine and intelligent writing of great promise."

> "I once was an Urchin, and lived on the street,
> Without either stockings or shoes on my feet,
> And at night cold and hungry, in dirt and in rags,
> I have cast myself down and have slept on the flags.
>
> I once walked the steps of St Michael's Place,
> And midst Meadow Angels, have come face to face —
> With ghosts from the graveyard and shrieks from the lairs
> What wonder I scampered and fell down those stairs."

The Critchlow family had consisted of five children, Kilby had informed me, with Frank being the youngest. Of the others, a sister and three brothers, two of the boys were in military service, one a soldier and the other in the Navy. The girl had taken a job in service and the remaining brother was married and lived in Stockport.

With the mother having been dead for some years, the responsibilities had fallen on the father, although little was known about him at the Homes except that his last address was shown to be in Liverpool. That the boys had had some connection with the Barnes Home at Cheadle and that the family had originated from Derbyshire, was all that Leonard Shaw could tell me. One incident concerning Frank Critchlow still lingers on and without too much difficulty I can picture him walking down the gangway of the large hall of the Peter Street YMCA where he took his turn on the platform to receive an award from the Rev. Benjamin Waugh. The occasion was the thirteenth annual meeting of the Manchester and Salford Boys' and Girls' Refuges, which was held at the YMCA in February of '82 and which was attended by the Lord Mayor and Bishop and Mrs Frazer, a gathering which not only attracted the city philanthropists but some of the country's leading debators of the children's issue. Included amongst the local supporters of the society were some familiar names and faces. There was William Mather, Frank Crossley, John Beith, Doctor Meacham, Doctor Boutflower, Edwin Gibb, Thomas Johnson and so many more. From where I had taken my vantage point that evening in the crowded assembly room, I was able to watch with more than a passing interest in the main event in connection with the boys and girls of the Strangeways Institution. Under the watchful eyes of Leonard Shaw, Richard Taylor and Gilbert Kirlew, all the children, including the Cheetham Orphan contingent, the Scarlet Uniformed Brigade, the blue jacketed Training Ship Sailors, and the girls from Heathfield, stood to attention while Mr Browne led them into a well rehearsed musical chorus of The Lord's Prayer.

The prize giving to the children in the Refuges and Homes had taken up a good deal of the evening with many of the awards being presented by either Doctor Barnardo or Benjamin Waugh, both guests of honour, and Mrs Birt of the Liverpool Sheltering Homes. Following a talk by Dr Bar-

nardo concerning the results and achievements of Manchester's own Refuge and its contribution to child reclamation, Kilby took several minutes to introduce his next guest and main speaker of the evening. "The Reverend Benjamin Waugh, author of the 'The Gaol Cradle'," he had said, "who together with Doctor Barnardo had visited our Cheetham Orphan Homes and Refuges today, has expressed a desire to become better acquainted with the Society, and in particular to learn more of the industrial work concerning boys and girls of school leaving age."

Although I had met the Rev Waugh on his previous visit to the Refuge, I could not help but feel once again drawn by his strong magnetic personality. He was a tall man with a good appearance, of strong physique and a gentle countenance. Again, I experienced the touch of his penetrating eyes as he searched the hall for answers to questions and again he displayed that same overwhelming offertory of genteelness which spilled from his bearded face like twinkling stardust. Despite his sombre cleric appearance, Benjamin Waugh, I reminded myself, was as far as I knew, the man who influenced many of the country's leading government ministers and Church leaders by bringing to their notice the inhumane cruelty and suffering experienced by the masses of poor children, who eked out an existence throughout the major cities. In particular, Mr Waugh had been instrumental in putting the children's case before the Magistrates, Poor Law Officers and Prison Governors, by means of his publication which referred in great detail to the plight of young children who were being locked up in prisons or sent to reformatories.

Rev. Benjamin Waugh of the NSPCC. By kind permission of the NSPCC.

In promoting his idealism and his own interpretation of a kind of children's charter, Benjamin Waugh was now becoming more prominently recognised for his present day support of the up and coming society which was establishing branches throughout the country. Known as the 'Society for the Prevention of Cruelty to Children', the SPCC's newly formed Manchester office, which was administered by the Boys' and Girls' Refuges and the amalgamated Childrens' Aid Society, earned both support from Mr Waugh and a commitment to its future existence. There was a suggestion, Mr Waugh had told Kilby, that the Society (SPCC) might one day become an integral part of the community and that the movement could become a national society. All this was in the future, he had said but, as far as London was concerned, Lord Shaftesbury had consented to become its first President and Samuel Smith, the Liverpool member of parliament, had agreed to take up the cause in the House.

The warmth of his sincerity and the justifiably strong arguments in favour of his involvement were more convincing now than at any other time.

Knowing Leonard Shaw and the Refuges had made my awareness of the plight of the street children more personal, and Benjamin Waugh's interpretation was a reality which I had, for one reason, or another, failed to acknowledge as a major crisis. Just once during the evening there was a reference to the Manchester Ragged Schools and the Earl of Shaftesbury's visit of 1866 when, as Lord Ashley, he laid the foundation stone of the new building in Charter Street.

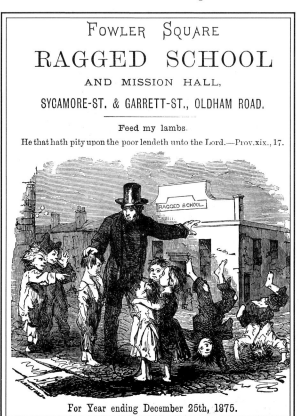

FOWLER SQUARE
RAGGED SCHOOL
AND MISSION HALL,
SYCAMORE-ST. & GARRETT-ST., OLDHAM ROAD.

Feed my lambs.
He that hath pity upon the poor lendeth unto the Lord.—Prov.xix., 17.

For Year ending December 25th, 1875.

I remember Thomas Johnson explaining in vivid detail how on the day before Lord Shaftesbury visited Angel Meadow, the notorious Blackley Street had had its name changed to Charter Street and all the street signs were replaced. He had laughed when he retold this episode, explaining that it was a moral whitewash and that the idea of the new name was supposed to give Angel Meadow an improved image. On a previous visit by Benjamin Waugh, there had been a meeting of the Manchester and Salford Ragged School Union which, compared to the vast audience of the Refuges meeting at the YMCA, was a small affair. Nevertheless, some of those same men whose genuine activity and dedication had inspired Mr Waugh were now themselves receiving inspiration.

Dotted amongst the attentive audience were several of those familiar faces. Alfred Alsop of Wood Street and Tommy Johnson and James Rutter of Charter Street were the more obvious names, but other personalities became evident as the evening wore on. Sharp Street and Heyrod Street were represented by Mr Aspinall and Mr Le Mare whilst not too distant sat John Moorhouse of Gravel Lane. The kind old face of Edwin Gibb, a Manchester man whom, it is said, was the founder of the city's first Sunday Ragged School, appeared next to his close associate John Shields. Casting my mind back I can remember Louis Hayes, a friend of Leonard Shaw's and a committee member of the Refuges, introducing me to this tender hearted and soft spoken philanthropist, who not only related how he and his friend James Brierley had opened their Ragged School in a rented front room in the Hulme district of Manchester, but how the movement had outgrown its humble beginnings. Tracing his past, Edwin Gibb, a man who reminded me so much of Thomas Wright, explained how in 1849 he began an open air mission for the hordes of children who roamed the streets and alleyways and, with the expectancy of a bitter winter and nowhere to shelter his band of Sunday ragged scholars, he found sanctuary in a kitchen in Cambridge Street which had been offered to him on a temporary basis. Some time after the winter months his friend James Brierley joined him on a regular basis and from that time on, his Sunday mission, which outgrew two other provisional homes, became firmly established as a Ragged School in Ormond Street.

With a growing membership and a call for unification throughout the Manchester and Salford areas, a massed meeting was held in the Free Trade Hall in April of 1858 by all the teachers and friends of the nine Ragged Schools of that time. Mr Robert Barnes, the well known philanthropist, whose generosity had brought about the first ever interdenominational assembly, agreed on that day to become the President of the newly formed Manchester and Salford Sunday Ragged School Union. In his declaration of the objectives of the new SRSU, he pointed out that its aims should be, — "to recognise no-one particular Christian denomination — only brotherly love and to encourage and help schools already in existence and to promote new schools until there is not a district uncovered or a child uncared for".

At the conclusion of that historic meeting, a statement declaring the general aims of the newly formed Union, was

ANNUAL RETURNS OF THE SCHOOLS

IN CONNECTION WITH THE

Manchester and Salford Sunday Ragged School Union, for the Year ending June 1886.

No.	Name and Locality of School	Names of Representatives	Superintendents	Teachers	Teachers' Average Attendance	Scholars' Average Attendance	Week Evening Classes Average Attendance	Sewing Class Average Attendance	Adult Bible Class Average Attendance	Penny Bank Amount Deposited (£ s. d.)	Penny Bank Interest (£ s. d.)	Penny Bank Amount Withdrawn (£ s. d.)	Scholars induced to attend Sunday School	Scholars become Teachers	Members in Band of Hope	Mission Services	Are Classes properly supplied with Teachers	Other Remarks
1	Ormond Street, Chorlton-on-Medlock	W. J. Booth	3	26	19	253		30		25 1 2		27 8 2					Fairly.	
2	St. Ann's, Queen Street, Deansgate	R. B. Taylor	2	22	18	500		6				10 9 5			150		Yes.	Library.
3	Sharp Street, Angel Meadow	J. Aspinall	4	29	21	340				33 14 8		734 18 6		4	300	20	Yes.	Working Men's Club; Saturday Evening Concerts; Mother's Meetings; Gospel Temperance Mission; Recreation Classes.
4	Heyrod Street, Ancoats	A. Le Mare	2	33	30	950	30	80	70	849 17 1							Fairly.	
5	Queen Street, Hulme	W. Court	3	18	16	216	30	15	8	107 6 2	2 11 8	129 10 2		6	150	100	Yes.	
6	Ellor Street, Pendleton	Samuel Bowden	3	29	20	327	15	15		149 2 5	2 0 6	108 7 10		3	80	110	Fairly.	Mothers' Meetings; Library; Choir.
7	Queen Street, Salford	M. S. Bowman	3	22	20	390				32 16 4	0 2 1	33 3 2		2	120		Fairly.	Tract Society; Library; Free Breakfast for Children.
8	Dark Lane, Ardwick	F. H. Bamford	2	24	20	349			4	93 3 4		74 13 9			49	50	Fairly.	
9	Broughton Road, Salford	H. Bowman	2	10	8	243		19		23 10 7	0 5 3	26 6 11			61	50	Fairly.	
10	Old Garratt, Princess Street	W. Hughes	1	24	19	291		24		25 5 9		27 18 1			158		No.	
11	Red Bank Little Scotland	J. Haygarth	1	18	16	217				21 17 1		18 13 0					Fairly.	
12	St. Mark's, Hulme	H. H. Mainwaring	1	17	14	211			25					10	350	35	Yes.	
13	Gravel Lane, Salford	J. T. Moorhouse	3	39	38	538	145	31		11 2 7		11 2 0			50	250	Fairly.	Free Breakfasts; Young Men's Society; Singing Class.
14	Gay Street	J. Jewett	3	22	11	182		13	65	209 2 2		112 1 6			175	120	No.	
15	Charter Street, Angel Meadow	Miss Brooks	4	42	40	905	183	30	75					4	100	600	Yes.	
16	Shaftsbury Institute	G. Locker	2	25	14	220		70	30					3	280	150	Yes.	Working Men's Club.
17	St. Catherine's, Collyhurst Road	R. Shuttleworth	2	15	13	206	50		30	120 19 1	1 6 0	89 19 1		1	102	130	Yes.	Drill Class; Choir.
18	Poland Street, Oldham Road	G. Porter	2	24	19	242	160	25	24	124 1 0		110 0 4			100	40	Yes.	Gospel Temperance Society.
19	Holland Street, New Islington	A. Baines	1	30	20	400	52	12		40 11 11		43 9 0					Yes.	
20	Ordsall, Salford	W. Coleman	1	14	12	230				143 19 0	2 0 0	150 0 10				100	No.	
21	Irwell Street	J. Liver	2	20	9	160	12	25	6	109 18 10		105 5 10		2	116	250	Yes.	
22	John Street, Pendleton	H. J. Richard	3	29	23	600			5	375 0 0	4 10 6	250 0 0				40	No.	
23	Boys' and Girls' Refuge	L. K. Shaw	2	9	6	110	40	50	12								Fairly.	
24	Saville Street, Chorlton-on-Medlock	T. Stockwell	1	22	5	190			12	223 14 10½	7 18 5	268 10 3½	2		120	120	Fairly.	
25	Openshaw	H. Southern	1	15	14	200			50						126	30	Fairly.	
26	Jackson Street	T. Bingham	3	19	17	262	50	30	40					4	280	200	Yes.	
27	Earl Street	J. Fox	4	18	17	220			16						60	80	Yes.	
28	McCormack Street	J. S. Langley	1	11	10	170			25						200	130	Yes.	
29	Bradford	J. Wemyss	1	14	12	130	300		50						300	450	Yes.	
30	Gorton Brook	J. Brown	2	24	18	250	40	12	10						50	100	Yes.	
31	Pilling Street	T. Turner	3	6	3	40									90	120	Fairly.	
32	Higher Openshaw, South St.	Wm. Salmon	1	3	3	70	100	10	10						100	50	Fairly.	
33	Cookson Street, Charlestown	E. Whiteley	1	10	10	120									50	40	Yes.	
34	Freehold Street, Pendleton	J. Slater	2	8	6	80									50	50	Yes.	
35	Gorton Street, Rochdale Road	R. E. D. Ewart	1	4	4	130									100		Fairly.	
			72	695	560	9942	1177	497	567	2761 4 11	19 0 10	2378 2 11½	2	39	3817	3295		

read to the vast audience:-

"Our aims are to lead the poor children in the paths of holiness and virtue; to instil into their minds the principles of that religion which shall prepare them for all the duties and exigencies of honest life — guide the energy of their youth — extinguish the flowers of unhallowed passion — smooth the rugged path of poverty — sweeten the cup of affliction — alleviate the pangs of dissolution — and finally, encircle the hoary head with a crown of glory."

I surmised that the ragged schools of Manchester and Salford were perhaps the only means of salvation for the thousands of pauper children in the city and I could understand why the link between the schools and the Boys' and Girls' Refuges was so strong. As Benjamin Waugh had said, in a brief reference to his much publicised statement regarding poor children's liberties and civil rights: "We are at the beginning of a parliament for children. The hour is great, and the greatness of the hour is equalled by the greatness of its difficulties".

Leonard Shaw's nodding of the head and approving glances at his fellow committee members was his way of echoing his own personal thoughts on a subject so near to his heart. Only recently he had conducted a survey on the streets of Manchester in order to bring to the attention of the city councillors the sad and depressing circumstances of young children who owed their existence to street hawking. In presenting his findings to the Manchester Corporation Kilby had sought the help of Mr Waugh in his attempt to bring about a new law which would prevent children selling their wares on the streets and begging into the early hours of the morning.

What Leonard Shaw had given as proof to the city council was a statement by the ten combined committee members of the Refuges who, over a period of three weeks, had accumulated a long inventory of Manchester streets and its young band of under-age hawkers. The conclusive evidence showed that, on an average day in Manchester within a quarter of a mile radius of Market Street, 181 boys and 48 girls under the age of ten years could be found begging or selling and that four times as many over the age of ten were in evidence. The Rev. Waugh had touched upon this issue more than once during his speech and in his sermon-like deliverance which begged for understanding and pity for Manchester children, used sentences which were becoming all too familiar. In his reference to the poverty and destitution of the poor areas of the city, he quoted his own version of the 'Cry of the Children' —

"A cry from fetid alleys
Where the sunbeams fear to shine
A cry from loathsome children
Where the outcast herd like swine;
A cry from lonely sick beds,
Where sufferers pine for death;
A cry from stifling garretts
Whose air is poisoned breath.
Oh! the bitter cry of children,

It keeps ringing in our ears;
The cry of outcast children,
Who can hear it without tears?

The cry of helpless women
The cry of hopeless men,
The cry of starving children
For food to nourish them;
A cry from dens of darkness
Where Satan's stronghold lies;
A cry from poisoned souls fast bound
With chains of slavery.

A cry that none can silence
A cry that nought can drown
A cry that rises night and day
From the sad heart of the town;
A cry for tender pity,
A cry for love and light;
A cry for help and healing
For freedom and for right.

Oh the bitter cry for children
It keeps ringing in our ears;
The cry of outcast children
Who can bear it without tears?"

That Benjamin Waugh had achieved so much for his cause was in my opinion due to his own understanding of his subject. The vibrations from his own commitment and activities were quite capable of moving the most hardened of society and the most stubborn natured of his audience. His stirring appeal, his forceful demands in the name of God, and his overall challenge to the assemblies, marked him as an individual whose conviction was his strength. If my assumptions were correct, Benjamin Waugh's formidable power lay in his one weakness, that of his love for outcast children and fellow men. Not surprisingly, Mr Waugh contributed his own poetry in aid of his cause, a fact which was not generally known, but somewhere hidden between the lines of those three verses lay a quality of wisdom and understanding which marked him out as a champion of human kindness:-

"He who checks a child in terror,
Stops its play, or stills its song
Not alone commits an error
But a grievous moral wrong.

Then give it play, and never fear it
Active life is not defect
Never, never break the spirit
Curb it only to direct.

Would you stop the flowing river?
Think you, it would cease to flow?
Onward it must go forever
Better teach it where to go."

CHAPTER NINE

You will be glad to know, Leonard, that I was at the funeral of our two Manchester boys. Through tender and misted eyes I attempted to fashion words to my reluctant thoughts which were by now in a state of turmoil. *It would seem that bathing is forbidden except twice a week, when a master goes with them, and sits all the time watching them, ready to jump in the river if any get into difficulty. The boys had, in the first instance, it seems, gone to pick up shellfish, and another boy persuaded them to go into the water to bathe.* I realised that with every word and every sentence, I was playing for time, and the delaying tactics were merely a ploy to avoid the inevitable. Lifting my head to gaze for a moment on the distant skyline of New Hampshire, I allowed my somewhat guilty mind, to wander along the tracks of the more memorable moments of the past two weeks. Somewhere in my personal belongings was a letter — already started before this tragedy — which described in detail the places of interest and the unusual occurrences of my American visit thus far. Perhaps one day in the future I would visit my favourite picnic spot near the old copper mines at Alderley Edge in England and spend an interlude recapturing the more pleasurable aspects of my holiday.

Casting my mind back to the Music Hall in Boston last Sunday, I remember meeting Mr Moody at his special mission service where, he had broken his summer's rest at Northfield to conduct the event. After tea at the Tremont House, I attended the meeting which brought back memories of the Manchester Free Trade Hall, especially the sight of the hundreds of people queuing outside a building which was already full to its 3000 capacity. After the service Mr Moody spent an hour shaking hands with old friends, many of them, I was told, converts of the Boston Mission of 1876. One in particular, had on the previous week given 50,000 dollars for the female seminary at Northfield. On the Monday, I accompanied Mr Moody back to Northfield to his home, and we were waved from the station by Mr and Mrs Dan Boyd of the Manchester House.

One thing which is so outstanding about America is the heat of the summer. Even here, on the Northfield hills, there is no escape, although my shaded position beneath the pines did at least offer a better prospect. "What do you think of this great country?" is the usual question asked of visitors to this continent, but the more topical question asked at this time of year is — "How do you stand the heat?" Truly, the heat is very great, varying from 94 to 105 degrees in the shade. Last week in New York, I was told, there were 86 cases of sunstroke of which 36 were fatal, and 700 infants were stated to have died from causes traceable to heat. Whilst in that city, I saw gentlemen going to their businesses in the early morning, their coats over their arms and in shirt sleeves. The men driving the buses and lorries were also in shirt sleeves, their heads protected by large umbrellas and their horses heads by two small umbrellas arranged one above the other. Ice water was found on every table and in every train. Stalls for the sale of iced lemonade were placed every few yards and opposite the City Hall stood a large tank on a cart marked 'Free Ice Water', provided by the businessmen of the city to encourage moderation.

The heat is such that it necessitates the doors and windows of houses to have screens fitted to keep out the mosquitos and other insects. I remember on one particular evening, spent in Vermont at a friends' house, being asked to delay my departure until a fire had been lit in the garden, the idea being to attract the insects away from the house before opening the doors. Only recently, Mr Moody had made reference to the so-called June bugs, and, on a lighter note, mentioned the recent visit of Mr Hodder of London who, whilst speaking in Northfield Church, had become distracted by the grey flying bugs almost the size of cockroaches, which occasionally dropped onto the bald head of one of his audience. Even Mr Hodder himself failed to escape the pests and Mr Pentecost, who was in the chair, was called to pluck two of the creatures from inside his collar. There are other insects called Lightening bugs, which give a bright flashing light as they fly about on hot summer nights. One amusing story which remains uppermost in my mind, and was told by Dwight Moody during the train journey, was of two men entering a small Western hotel who, on signing their names in the hotel register, saw a bed bug crawl across the page. "Well!" said one traveller to the other, "That's the first time I ever saw a bug looking for the number of your room!" On my visit to Washington, still as intensely hot as Boston and New York, I found it none the less extremely pleasant. The avenues of Washington all radiate from the Capitol like the spokes of a wheel, and the foliage is so dense in the treelined avenues that the shade is delightful. The Capitol is a magnificent white marble building with statuary, and all the government buildings including the White House are remarkable.

The population of Washington, I am told, is 150,000, being 100,000 white people and 50,000 black people. I was particularly impressed by the magnificent coloured costumes worn by the latter, so evident on the street cars and steamers.

If I were asked to give a perference to the county which impressed me more than any other, I would have to choose the excursion from Vermont, through the famous White Mountain Notch to North Conway in New Hampshire, a journey which gave a view of the Mounts Willard, Layfette, Monroe, Franklin, Lincoln, Webster and Washington. The railway I travelled on ran high up one side of the Notch, showing the mountains on both sides, and the valley between, densely clothed with trees, while on the opposite side I could see waterfalls like silver ribbons, falling a thousand feet down. About half way through the Notch is an old house to which excursions are made, called the Willey House, after a family which had once lived there. One day in 1826, hearing a landslide above the house, the members of this family had rushed out, leaving the baby in the cradle. A rock near the house had parted the slide and the house and baby escaped, but the rest of the family had been buried under hundreds of tons of earth and stones. Through the White Mountain district, the train stops at four celebrated hotels, the Fabian, the Crawford, the Twin Mountain and the Mount Pleasant, all under one management, connected by railway, mail, telegraph and telephone and capable of accommodating thirteen hundred guests.

Before meeting Mr Moody at Boston, I had spent an evening with some old friends now living in the Massachusetts city of Lowell, famous for its cotton mills. I shall always treasure the memory of that Saturday evening, walking down the crowded streets and hearing the familiar Lancashire dialect spoken by Lancashire operatives who had emigrated from their home towns of Rochdale and Oldham. The nostalgia of that time had been almost unbearable, and that same deep emotion which had surfaced during a period of homesickness in the company of my Lowell friends was in some ways reminiscent of my present conflict.

Lowering my gaze to the Connecticut Valley shimmering in the heat of the early sun, I focussed my attention on the bend of the river where the boys had met their deaths. The reason, I concluded, for avoiding mention of the boys' names was due in some way to the overwhelming feeling of personal loss, a tragedy which had burdened me with an unwelcome responsibility.

The very mention of little Austin Morris and George Tobin was so painful that for a moment I shuddered with guilt at their deaths. Could fate have brought me to Mount Hermon at this very hour, I mused? Was I not the very person who had found little George in Manchester and shared in a similar rescue with his friend Austin? These reflections were not only true, but so uncanny that for a moment I was tempted to close my eyes and pinch myself in the hope that this was all a bad dream. My damp handkerchief and my unshakable memory of the funeral service proved enough to confirm my saneness in the matter and once again I tried to focus my thoughts on the two former little urchins I had come to know and love over the past eighteen months.

Whitsuntide in Albert Square, a little over fifteen months previously, is a memory which I will always cherish, particularly when I think of Austin and George, whose happy and smiling faces in the procession indicated to me that they had wiped away the unpleasant recollection of their early life, such as it was. In fact, both of them had become so much a part of the orphan family at Cheetham Hill that anyone unaware of their past history would assume them to be no more than just a couple of school pals intent on the normal pursuits of juvenile excitement. However bright and cheerful was the look on George Tobin's face, holding on to the ropes of the Refuge banner, I could not resist the urge to compare the fortunes of George when our paths had first crossed in the suburbs of Manchester, a meeting which I now regarded as one of the most unusual events in my life.

The start to that year in 1883 had been one of great excitement. Echoes from the chiming cathedral bells had followed me as I had walked down Millgate to Hunts Bank and from there to the Strangeways Refuges. On arrival at the Frances Street Home to partake of the New Year's Day breakfast, I was confronted by a policeman in conversation with Mr Browne and several groups of boys engaged in what appeared to be a street cleaning exercise. Once in the building, Mrs Browne informed me that the early morning

gales had not only removed many of the roof tiles but had also brought down the enormous 'Refuge' sign from the top of the institution building with such a thunderous bang, that many of the neighbourhood residents had rushed out of their homes to view the chaos. Not to be distracted by the excitement of the unusual events being enacted, I listened intently to the after-breakfast speeches by members of the committee, all of whom, apart from wishing every resident and friend of the Refuges a Happy New Year, had become engrossed in the ritual known as 'messages for the New Year'. From what Kilby had to say about various Refuge innovations and forthcoming events, 1883 looked all set to be an exciting year ahead, "a year" Kilby said, "when we shall once again share in the Manchester reception and homecoming of Dwight Lyman Moody." I, for one, could not help but acclaim this marvellous New Year news and share in the sentiment which Kilby had inferred in connection with his friend of the past decade. Nearer to home and the present was the subject of the 'poor' and 'delicate' little girls of Manchester who as yet had not received all the attention they were entitled to. "This has now been remedied," said Kilby. "Plans are well in hand to rent a house in Warton Road, Lytham, which, when completed this year, will accommodate twenty girls and will be known as 'The Sea-Side Home for the Little Children.'"

Having digested the Moody news and having taken in all the subsequent items of itinerant Refuges agenda, a mood of optimism and preoccupation took over during the finale of the breakfast assembly. There must have been at least three hundred boys in the hall, some in scarlet and some in blue, depending on the industry in which they were employed, whilst most wore the velvet cord suits of the Refuges. As custom dictated, wives of the committee members brought the New Year's breakfast meeting to a close, with a few words chosen from a well-known reading text. This New Year, the honour had been given to Marianne Kirlew (sister of the new committee member, Gilbert Kirlew), who informed the audience that she had written the following verse as her contribution to the January edition of the 'Christian Worker' magazine:

> "The old year has gone, with its trials and sorrows;
> The new in its youth, and its brightness is here;
> Then let us receive in the hour of its freshness,
> To usefully, lovingly, live through 'this year.'"

The blustery biting winds were still howling as I left the Frances Street building en route for the YMCA office of the Hospital Flower Mission. Ahead of me lay a full morning's work delivering bunches of flowers to patients at Crumpsall Infirmary and Workhouse, followed by a short visit to the Monsall Park Hospital and Ancoats Hospital.

Fortunately the texts and verses had been written out the previous day, which meant that the usual hustle and bustle was unnecessary and my journey in the laden brougham could, if the horse so desired, progress at a steady trot. Swaying to the motion of the cab and applying the regular rhythm of clip-clopping to my own mood, I became entranced by the vision of possibilities arising from the news of the impending visit by the great evangelist from America. It is almost ten years since his great revival meetings in Britain, I thought, and Manchester is still reaping untold benefits even to this day.

So far as I was aware, Kilby had been keeping notes of Dwight Moody's evangelistic tours and it came as no surprise when he informed me that Moody had spent at least five months of the 1881/2 winter in Scotland, especially in the Glasgow and Edinburgh areas. After preaching in Paris and holidaying in Switzerland, he had begun another tour of Britain, beginning in South Wales and taking in the South of England on his journey northward. The reference at the breakfast table by Kilby to Dwight Moody's "homecoming" had now coincided with my thoughts on a recently related story concerning Mr Moody and Henry Moorhouse, a story which appealed to my sense of patriotism, in the light of Mr Moody's display of affection towards the Manchester people. Henry Moorhouse, a Manchester man and well known Evangelist, had passed away at his Ardwick home during the Christmas period of 1880 and, like many other people, I had grieved at the loss of the 40 year old crusader who had won world-wide recognition. According to the story, the young looking Henry Moorhouse had claimed the attention of Dwight Moody during a crusade in Dublin, where he had been christened — 'The Great Boy Preacher'. Some time later, during the early 1860s, Henry Moorhouse had begun a tour of the American continent, and it was in Chicago that Dwight Moody had come under the influence of Henry Moorhouse, the 'Boy Preacher'. So too had Mr Moody learned of the conversion of his new friend, and of his early upbringing on the Manchester streets, "a period," he claimed, "when I had revelled as an Ardwick ruffian and tormented the Ragged School teachers at Heyrod Street". However, it was Henry Moorhouse's mastery of the bible and the message in his preaching which had caused Dwight Moody to rethink his own future, so much so that, from that time on, Mr Moody had based much of his philosophy on the teaching and ministry of Henry Moorhouse.

Some time later in the day, when my hospital visits had culminated at Monsall, and deciding to clear my mind of the sights I had witnessed that morning, I decided to walk through the Oldham Road dwellings on my way to the Philips Park cemetery. A promise to a dying patient in the men's ward of the workhouse had resulted in this last errand of the day, that of laying a bunch of flowers on the grave of his former wife. Entering the cemetery from the gates on Hulme Hall Lane, I made my way down to the plots nearest the river, a section now familiar, and where on previous occasions I had witnessed the burials of several Manchester paupers. Having completed my errands I paused for a moment to draw the ribbon of my bonnet a little tighter. The wind and the particles of wet snow had discouraged me from staying longer and, turning my head for a last glimpse of the riverside resting place, uttered a few chosen words of sympathy. Looking back at the moment I am tempted to use the

word fate for, although my pause had amounted to only a few seconds, what transpired during that brief interlude was the beginning of a whole new chapter in my life.

Between the crescendo of the next gusting wind and the momentary silence created in the wake of the previous squall, a faint whimpering resembling the crying of a child caught my attention. There, not many yards from where I stood, I saw what appeared to be a boy sat on a gravestone, his head resting on his knees and his sobbing coming in such deep bursts, his whole frame seemed to shudder with every intake and exhalation of breath. In next to no time, I was by his side with words of comfort and a clean white handkerchief to wipe away the tears. My heart ached for the little fellow and I desperately wanted to clasp him to my bosom but owing to his filthy condition I adopted the more cautionary alternative. In answer to my questions he told me his name was George and he had come to visit his mother, the same woman who was now resting beneath the stone he was sitting on. When he disclosed the fact that he had no father and that he was "lodging in't Medder," I knew then that I had to take some responsibility. There were so many other questions I wanted to put to him but I decided they could wait in view of the coldness of the day and the shivering image sitting before me. My mind was now made up. I would take the cab to the Refuges and ask Walter Browne to give him overnight shelter whilst urging Leonard Shaw to make further inquiries into his welfare.

According to little George, he was about ten years of age, a fact which he disclosed to me on the way back to Strangeways. Sitting in the cab and taking stock of the waif, who by now had relinquished the tears in favour of his interest in horses, I observed what Kilby would have described as a typical Deansgate street urchin. Quoting Leonard Shaw's own words: "This is a child who wanders from place to place without any fixed dwelling or guardianship; who grows up in ignorance on the streets, and who manages to exist each day without any visible means of support."

I recalled to mind a verse I had once written and subscribed to the Refuges magazine, a verse which suddenly seemed to have found a new meaning:

"To take the little wanderers from the street, —
To cleanse, to clothe, to shoe their naked feet, —
To be a friend to those whose friends are gone, —
To find a home for those who else had none, —
To feed the hungry and, all else above,
To teach them the truth of Jesus' love, —
To take them from that fearful school of vice,
The Streets, where darkest sin their steps entice, —
To draw them lovingly from such a life, —
To guide, to aid them in a nobler strife."

Once in the warmth of the Refuges waiting and reception room and in possession of a cup of warm coffee, George Tobin projected a sorry looking picture. Set against the immaculately polished woodwork and the ever so clean curtains and table cloths, the image of George became blacker by the minute. Beginning at the top, the thick long hair all matted on top, hung over his sallow complexion. If there was an outstanding feature about George, it was his large dark eyes which, whilst reflecting a tendency to mischief and humour, also spoke of a forlorn sadness too deep to explore at the present moment. The only neatness about the rest of his attire was his neck scarf, a type of workman's neckerchief similar to that a navvy would wear.

From then on down, a jacket which had seen better days on a much older and taller person hung loosely over his shoulders, attempting to hide the two pieces of string which held up his trousers. Even these were not serving the purpose for which they were meant. One leg of the pants almost touched the floor whilst the other, torn and in ribbons, hung loosely over the knee like a shredded flag blowing from the mast. If shoes were the mirror of a man's fortune, then it was obvious that little George had not yet made his mark in the big world. At another time and under different circumstances the sight of the little mite's footwear would have caused me to break into laughter. As it was, the pathetic figure before me boasted only of a left footed half-clog which had outworn itself, and a right footed button up boot several sizes too big. As there was no toecap to the boot, the size didn't seem to matter that much. His cap which he nervously passed continually from one hand to the other was so screwed up that one could be excused for mistaking it for a floor cloth. "Now then, George," said Mr Browne, unaware of all the details which I had gleaned from the boy, "What's this I hear about your mother? Has she left you, or where is she?" I bit my lip as I glanced at George and cursed myself for not telling Walter Browne the whole story. At the mention of the word 'mother' the flood gates of tears were opened and

little George, surrounded by the sympathy and warmth of caring, broke down under the heavy sobbing which threatened to bring him to his knees. Both Mrs Browne and myself comforted George until he was able to continue, but by this time Mr Browne in his wisdom suggested that a hot bath and scrub would be of benefit to all concerned, a fact which needed no seconding.

Within the hour George had reappeared, looking bright and cheerful and glowing like a new penny. A further helping of coffee and warm buns not only revived his flagging spirit, but revived a confidence which had until this moment remained buried. The new George Tobin or 'my New Year boy', a title I had secretly christened him, now complete with a new pair of clogs and properly fitting clothes, became more assured in himself and more able to tell Walter Brown a little about himself.

"Please, Sir, Mother's bin dead about five months," he began. "Afore Mother died, our Meg and me lived in a little room near't Cathedral; there was nowt much in; I slept in't corner on a bit of straw. Fayther come 'ome sometimes, but always be'avin' and swearin' cos he was aller's drunk. Then mother ud ketch hold on us, and run wi' us, and stop out till Fayther was sleepin'. When he were at home a bit, I used to have a go wi' him and shove t'cart, and shout 'errin's', 'cabbage', 'salt', or owt he was sellin'. Last time he were away, mother tuk ill and she died; t'nabours said it were his fault. Somebody took her away in a box; me and Meg followed um and watched um put mother in a big hole, a man said summat' and we came away. When we was cryin' a lot, some folks said — "Poor things", and give us a copper and told us to go home. We went back t'a empty room and slept on't straw that night. Next day t'nabours took us to Swinton

Waiting for the procession in Albert Square. Drawing by: H. E. Tidmarsh.

Manchester Whit Walks in Mosley Street, showing the Art Gallery and St Peter's Church. Drawing by: H. E. Tidmarsh.

The Orphan Homes at George Street, Cheetham Hill, in the 1880's. NB: Although the houses have long since gone, the wall is still preserved.

Schools. We 'adn't been in long, afore Fayther fetched us out, an' tuk another room in Long Millgate, next door to 'th'owd houses, yer know, near't Crown and Cushion. We got some straw and stayed there til Fayther went off again, and me and Meg got chucked out. Meg went to live wi' an aunt and I got took to Crumpsall wukhus'. When another lad ran away he took me with him to lodgins in't 'Medder'. A nabour said me Fayther had died an' I would have to go to' reformatory, but I slept out with a lad in Charter Street instead."

This, then, was George Tobin's story, a revelation which would have to be confirmed before his permanent acceptance at the Refuges. Before leaving the Strangeways home that evening, I couldn't resist the urge to say a final 'goodnight' to George, and peeping through the door of the cubicle, observed a contented little boy, snugly wrapped in a warm bed, probably for the first time in months. Looking back on this chapter in my life and the New Year episode served only to confirm what I already felt about a year which had been filled with exhilaration and excitement from its very commencement.

Transferring my thoughts again to the Whitsuntide procession, I remembered thinking on how the day had blossomed out of the grey skies of the early morning daybreak in the city. At half past seven that morning on my way to the Peter Street office, I had observed the policemen from Minshull Street clearing the Albert Square of people and erecting barriers at strategic corners of the perimeter. By the time I had returned after eight, the Square had been transformed into a pseudo-military parade ground with marshalls and policemen all around. To describe the whole day and all the events which took place would no doubt fill a news column of the daily papers, whereas my notes written for the benefit of the Strangeways Society were more precise and relevant:

"Monday 14th May — Whit Week, 1883. As I write, the strains of more than one of the many Whit Week bands are sounding in my ears, and on all fronts Manchester is keeping high holiday. It is the children's holiday festival, long anticipated and filled with hopes and fears; but thanks to the weather, which had been very congenial up to Sunday, and on that night changed for the better, the fears were dispelled, and hope reigned supreme as thousands of little ones rose with the lark, donned their 'Sunday best', and wended their way to their various schools, en route to the Albert Square rendezvous.

While the separate deputations of the army of young people were uncurling their banners and making ready for the march, preparations to receive the masses in the square were now well advanced. First of all, the cobbles were sprinkled with red sand, in view of the unsteady little feet. Then, the boys of the News Brigade from the Boys' Refuges were posted at each corner of the square as markers from the column which would be formed later on, their scarlet jackets making ideal identification stations. By a quarter past eight the Town Hall square had been made ready, and no sooner had the clock chimed when in marched the Drum and Fife Band of the Refuges followed by the boys of the Caxton and News Brigades. The white jackets of the 'Indefatigable' sailor

boys and the smart uniform of the 'Shoe Black' Brigade, completed the Strangeways contingent. After a lull of ten minutes the torrent of children's armies poured into the square.

St Mary's of Deansgate was the first group to arrive, its banner draped in mourning for the deceased wife of the Rev. Atkinson. The large procession of neat and tidy children belonging to the blue banner of Ancoats 'All Souls' Church School was next, followed by the first appearance of the new Church of St Clement, of Broughton Lane. Behind them, Cross Street was like a surging parti-coloured sea with the new Wood Street Banner rippling in the breeze as each wave swept in on the Albert Square. The masses of children and adults, like the waves in the Laureate's poem, swayed even in rest and, with the continual new arrivals, there was soon a lively, simmering sea, in which the only sure and fixed elements of order were the posts manned by the boys in scarlet.

Prior to leaving Albert Square, the National Anthem was taken up by the multitudes, and then the procession started off in earnest, en route to the final destination, the Manchester Cathedral. In a veil of weak sunshine and dust blowing in the wind, the robed boys of Cheetham's Hospital and Cathedral Clergy set off along Princess Street. It seemed that all Manchester was gathered into the mile or so of streets along the route, and the cheers and hand clapping became almost deafening. Not a single space was to be seen along a highway which had now become the traditional route of the Whit Walks. Heading the main body of witnessers and adopting the leading position, came the smartly uniformed band of the Ardwick Industrial Schools which was followed further down the column by the boys of the Barnes Home Band. After what seemed like an eternally long march along Princess Street, Mosley Street, Market Street, Market Place and Old Millgate, the tired but happy little wanderers arrived at the Cathedral gates, where the march was disbanded."

When the tired and hungry contingent belonging to the Refuges arrived in the courtyard of Cheetham's School, they were divided into their respective groups, and after a short rest made their way to the Strangeways home, another half mile along Great Ducie Street. Since the older boys of the brigades had departed to the YMCA in Peter Street for a dinner in the company of the Lord Mayor, the normally active Refuge building had been reduced to a third of its capacity.

Over a welcome dinner table, with the orphan children directly in front and the remaining children on one side, I had ample opportunity to reflect on the success of the morning, a day which so far had lived up to its happy reputation. Row upon row of smiling talkative boys and girls not only testified to their enjoyment of the dinner and pudding but radiated a great satisfaction on the day which marked the beginning of their holiday.

In his professional capacity, Mr Browne had been called upon to submit two or three paragraphs to the St John's Parish magazine, describing his news and views of the Whit

Walks in connection with the children of Cheetham Hill. Displaying his usual artistic talent, Walter Browne included his impression of the George Street children, a sketch which depicted the orphan group with banner raised, waiting for the order to depart from Cheetham's courtyard near the Cathedral. This picture, signed with the usual WTB monogram, became a great favourite with the children and in due course became a framed treasure of the Atkinson Orphan Home.

"Our little men and little women," wrote Walter Thurlew Browne, "had a hard day's work on Whit Monday. Not only did they march with the Refuge boys in the morning procession through town, but in the evening they joined in the smaller gathering of the Cheetham Hill Schools in company with the children of St Luke's. Their little banners with their touching inscription 'Little Orphan Boys' Homes' and 'Little Orphan Girls' Homes' attracting attention from the sympathetic ladies and gentlemen in Broughton Park, wended their way to the large school room of St John's. Annie Doyle and Rachael Launders, residents of the Crossley Home, were the proud leaders of the girls' column, whilst at a respectable distance at the rear marched the boys, their banners held high by the two Atkinson Home boys, George Tobin and Austin Morris."

It seemed to me that little George Tobin was determined to hang on to his banner for as long as his grasp would let him, a fact which contributed to his exuberance of pride and elation. After all, this Whitsuntide Festival had provided him with both a holiday and a feeling of importance for the first time in his life. Gazing at the group as they left the park at the John Street entrance, my thoughts reflected on the general happiness and well being of most of the eighty or so George Street children whose past histories of darkness and despair were now but a faded memory.

Austin Morris, the other half of the banner carrying duo, and now a close friend and ally of his associate George Tobin, was quite a sturdy fellow for a small boy who was not yet ten years of age. His eagerness to run errands and his capacity to absorb a day's work with untiring cheerfulness had become his hallmark at the orphanage. However, the demeanour of Austin Morris had not always been so popular at the Refuges, neither had his attitude, especially within his first few months of rehabilitation. Austin, like many of the Refuges family of boys and girls, had suffered not only the loss of a close family at an early age, but had endured months of physical and mental cruelty, an experience which had left wounds to the body and scars to the mind. Thanks to the watchful eyes and experienced mind of Gilbert Kirlew of the 'Childrens' Aid Society and 'Refuges Committee', Austin had been rescued, in the words of Leonard Shaw, "at his most vulnerable age and not a moment too soon."

According to Mr Kirlew, the strange story of Austin Charles William Morris — a name written on a fragmented piece of paper relating to his birth — unfolded in Southport in July of 1882. Relating to this incident through the pages of the Refuges' monthly edition of the Christian Worker, Gilbert Kirlew in his special chapter entitled 'An Adventure with Street Waifs in Southport', quoted almost word for word his meeting with young Austin.

'Can you spare a copper, Sir?' If the words had been addressed to me in Market Street, or even in some of the back streets of Manchester's bustling environment, I should not have been surprised, but they were drawled out by a ragged and miserable little boy on the fashionable promenade of Southport, where one would naturally expect to be free from the importunate appeals of the 'street urchin'.

I had been but a few hours enjoying the quiet of this truly delightful and highly respectable seaside resort, when I became aware of the presence of the same class of children among whom we labour in Manchester.

Again, 'Can you spare a copper, Sir?' and the little round face with bright twinkling blue eyes, looked up into mine. There were two other lads begging from the passers-by but the well dressed crowds sauntered past or lounged on the seats, enjoying the view of the golden beaches and drinking the fresh sea air. Hardly any notice was being taken of the trio whose shoeless, ragged and perhaps hungry appeals were now directed to where I was sitting. The two older boys, having assumed a solemn aspect and still cautious in their approach, ventured within a few yards of where I was sitting and near enough for me to overhear their comments. "I know wot-e-is; 'e's a slop," (meaning a police officer) in street vernacular. "No e's not," said his pal, "E's t' do wit' school board." The little one nearest to me and now with his back turned towards me, contributed his own interpretation of the situation. "Bet e's to do wit' formatory, thats wot e' is, ar know." With a reassuring smile and a little coaxing with the aid of a few comic books, I succeeded in enticing the three lads closer to me. Learning that I was in no way connected with the police or the school board, and finding to their delight that I was acquainted with their language, fears became subdued and soon we were all good friends.

First, I was introduced to Alfie, the twelve year old leader of the group. "Yes Sir, ar'ave a mother but she gets drunk and 'Warms us'." With further questioning, he replied, "A 'ome? I aint got one, ar'live in lodgins in Preston. Sometimes I've walked to Bolton and Liverpool and Blackburn on tramp. Once, I walked to Manchester but that's long time sin." "Please Sir," said the boy calling himself Tommy Flynn, "When Alfie comes to Manchester he stays wi' us in't Meadow. Last time he came we went shoe blacking near't Exchange and got run off wit' school board. Now't weather's better we've come to make our fortune near't piers at Southport and Blackpool, and a've brought me pal with us to 'elp us, cos 'ese got nowhere to live, that's why we're asking for coppers Sir, for lodgins." Glancing at his pal, the little fellow standing nearest to me and obviously unsure of himself and the situation, I said, "What is your name?" "Where are your parents?" "Why are you begging?" There was a negative response to all three questions, and the long silence which followed confirmed my thoughts on the situation. Before I had a chance to act upon my instincts, Alfie had put his arm across the shoulders of his little friend and in a protective manner pronounced that young Austin was an orphan with nobody to look after him, and that was why Tommy had brought him from Manchester a few days ago.

Fearing that all three of them would disappear before I had a chance to finish explaining the benefits of regular work, regular meals and a warm clean bed at the Manchester Home, I reluctantly agreed to give them a few hours to make a decision and to meet me at the Boundary Street Mission at Birkdale, where a free meal and a night's lodgings could be had. At 6.30 that evening there was no sign of the three urchins and the chapel service went ahead as usual with its offering of salvation to the tramps and lodging house poor of Southport. Towards the end of the Sunday evening meeting, a faint knocking was heard at the entrance doors, and as the heads of the small congregation turned to enquire at the intrusion, a steward was seen to emerge from the doorway, leading the culprit into the mission hall. It was little Austin, in his bedraggled and barefoot state and crying for all he was worth. His explanation for the commotion, a tale he was able to tell after the comforting reassurance of the elders had reduced his sobs, was that his pals had brought him to the mission, knocked on the doors and run off and left him. The absence of the two runaways was a great concern but in view of the fact that little Austin had been rescued, gave cause for great jubilation.

"'Tis the 'Cry of the Children' calling
Calling to God on high
The voice of the streets uprising
Oh, help us or we die;

They know not the joy of sunshine
Nor the spring of the flowery turf;
By the stagnant pools of human life,
They long for the gladsome surf.

And their captive eyes in the cells of sin
Peer forth from the grated bars
But see no love in the daybreak,
No peace in the holy stars.

The children they are calling
Tend us, save us, ere we fall,
Give us hope and send your blessings,
Thy tender mercies over all."

To continue the story; the Monday before noon, one of the quieter periods of the Refuges when preparations were in progress to make ready for the returning and hungry brigade boys, Mr Kirlew, already behind schedule for his Monday morning committee meeting, made his entrance from the Frances Street doorway into the quieter recesses of the reception room. At his side and clutching his hand for some reassurance trotted a small ragged boy of tender age, the same boy, I was to learn later, who had been rescued at Southport and brought back to Manchester and who appeared to be in need of protection.

When Gilbert Kirlew explained the unusual circumstances surrounding little Austin, I remembered thinking that, although one or two children had in the past arrived at the Refuges from Dr Barnardo's in London and Mr Quarrier's in Glasgow, Austin was the first child to be rescued at such a distance from his home town. Again on reflection, I was reminded that Manchester was not, correctly speaking, Austin's home town or birthplace and neither was he a northerner. Back in the Strangeways reception home where the bewildered Austin nibbled at a large jam filled cake and where his future was being discussed at great lengths by the committee, I observed a boy who supposedly was a true orphan with no living relatives and who, like most little Manchester street wanderers, had found his way into the lodging area of Angel Meadow. Later that afternoon, when the ablutions and outfitting had been completed, and when, in true Barnardo fashion, little Austin had been photographed in the 'before' and 'after' pose, I was requested by Leonard Shaw to accompany Mr Kirlew the very next day, on a mission to verify the facts as related by Austin and to establish the true identity of the little mite.

Whilst awaiting the arrival of Gilbert Kirlew who had business with Dr Meacham at the Charter Street surgery, I became engrossed in my surroundings and quite unthinkingly called to mind some of the many stories which had contributed to the Meadow's notoriety. Most of the historical rhetoric had emanated from my departed friend Thomas Wright and it was he who, in my younger days, had issued a stern warning against entering Angel Meadow without an accomplice. "This spot," he had once said, referring to the Ducie Bridge and Long Millgate corner where now stood the round fronted building of 'my uncle's' (pawnshop), "was considered to be the gateway to Yorkshire by coach and horses and this was the route used by Charlotte Bronte before the steam train era." Knowing of Thomas Wright's fondness of the Brontes and of his personal friendship with Mrs Gaskell, a close associate of Charlotte Bronte, I reflected on the sadness I had experienced at the time Thomas Wright had learned of their untimely deaths.

'Scotland Bridge', 'Little Scotland', 'Gibraltar', 'Orange Valley' and 'Redbank', all names connected with this locality, had been explained to me by several people connected with the Refuges, each one applying their own enthusiastic version of the Irk and Angel Meadow and the part it played during the early days of the Industrial Revolution. One of those enthusiasts, another personal friend of Thomas Wright's, was Thomas Brittain, a former superintendent of the Ardwick Industrial School and the founder member of Manchester's first 'ragged school' in Nelson Street, Angel Meadow. Although he was a Yorkshireman, I surmised that there was very little that Thomas Brittain did not know about his adopted Manchester and his knowledge and exuberance in matters of local interest proved to be useful and

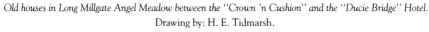

Old houses in Long Millgate Angel Meadow between the "Crown 'n Cushion" and the "Ducie Bridge" Hotel.
Drawing by: H. E. Tidmarsh.

supportive in many a boardroom debate. It was he who had provided me with a brief introduction to Manchester's 17th and 18th century architecture in 'Gibraltar' and 'Scotland' and I distinctly remember him paying a special reference to the old timbered cottages in Long Millgate, almost opposite to where I was waiting. Mr Cohen and family, whose textile business advertisement claimed a large portion of the whitewashed exterior of the old dwellings, appeared to owe their survival to the so called modern cottages leaning inwards from Munday Street at the one end, and the firm foundations of the 'Crown and Cushion' at the other.

When Mr Kirlew arrived, his delay caused by the daily prayer meeting called by Dr Meacham as part of his surgery practice, he was in the company of one of the teachers of Charter Street School, who agreed to escort us safely through the Meadow.

At the junction of Angel Street and Ashley Lane, our escort paused for a moment and pointing to the railings and the stone wall of St Michael's Place, informed us that this was the spot where bones and skulls, remnants of the mass burials during the plagues, had surfaced during the great floods of twenty years before. Also, just opposite Nelson Street within the walled recess, were the Angel Steps, so called because of the many apparitions of angels witnessed by the local inhabitants, who assumed that they were there to guard the graves of the many hundreds of infants. This introduction to the famed Angel Steps not only interrupted my train of thought but brought to mind a verse which had been recently quoted at a riverside internment at Phillips Park cemetery:-

"Infant's graves are steps of angels
Where earth's brightest gems of innocence repose,
God is their parent, and they need no tears;
He takes them to his bosom from earth's woes."

Following the steep ascent of Angel Street as far as the bend where St Michael's stood, Mr Kirlew suggested that this was where, in his opinion, his enquiries should begin. Standing in the middle of the worn cobbled street — a spot which used to be known as 'Ranters Hill' on account of the moralizing from the Baptist Church at the top of the hill — and looking downwards from the grimy and unsightly church, I began to sense the oppressive elements of the neighbourhood, a gloom and doom of which I had so often been reminded. There was no denying that my usual high spirits were now on the decline and that the sun's early morning rays were already dimming in the atmosphere of the district. Even at this early hour the obnoxious smells from the Irk and Irwell and the Gould Street gas works were living up to their reputation, combining to prove beyond doubt that this was indeed a living hell. When one considered that the mixture also included the aromas from the tannery, the dyeworks, the iron foundry, the brewery, the tripe works, and rotting vegetation from the Smithfield market, all added together with the neighbourhood's fried fish and bad sanita-

Another view of Long Millgate, Angel Meadow. Circa 1900. Courtesy, Manchester Central Library.

St. Michael's flags Angel Meadow — a sad reminder of the hardship and suffering of 19th Century Manchester.
Photo: Courtesy of the City Engineer, Manchester.

tion smells, one would agree that the cauldron of Angel Meadow was indeed a potent brew.

The fascination of the burial ground, also known as "the Flags" was irresistible and I pondered on the awful conditions of Manchester during the era of the plague. According to rumour, there were well over forty thousand bodies beneath the stones, all victims of poverty and sickness, whose mass grave had from time to time been plundered by fellow humans and the elements. 'Tommy' Johnson's recital of the great fight in Angel Meadow, a story I had heard on many occasions, suddenly became reality as I gazed at the Flags and espied the ghostly images of 'Stumpy' and 'Bacup Billy', the two local characters who had fought a duel to the death in a so called 'up and down' boxing match many moons ago.

The waiting over, and as far as I was concerned not a moment too soon, Mr Kirlew had located a house on Angel Street where the kind and Christian-like lodging house proprietors — "one of the few decent families of the street," he had pointed out later — reluctantly confirmed that Austin Morris, a stranger to the district, had lodged in the Meadow for several days before setting off with his pal, "on tramp." So far as Austin's previous whereabouts were concerned, only the name, a Mrs Pritchard, and a street off London Road, had been mentioned. Signifying that this information was sufficient and that the mission to the Meadow was complete, we continued our journey uphill to the Rochdale Road exit, a rather hurried departure and one which solicited the cautious stares of the street inhabitants, whose doorstep

meetings had now escalated into a major inquiry concerning our presence.

After thanking our escort from Charter Street and bidding him 'Good-day', we set off on the remainder of our journey, to the London Road vicinity, an expedition which began in the bustling Smithfield market off Swan Street, skirting the busy thoroughfare of Ancoats Lane, until the terminus at Fairfield Street and Dark Lane. Comparing the infamous district we had just visited and our present location in Back Acton Street, the area, though still of a considerably poor class, was a definite improvement. Over a cup of tea in the front parlour of number fourteen, Mrs Pritchard gave her version of little Austin, "A poor little tot," she said, "who needed a good home."

Within the hour it was time to leave the neighbourhood, but not before Gilbert Kirlew had extracted every little scrap of information concerning little Austin. The story had not only proved Austin's status as an orphan, but had thrown light on many of the sordid details surrounding the pathetic conditions under which he had survived. According to the good hearted and sympathetic Mrs Pritchard, (a woman who had openly wept tears of joy on hearing of Austin's rescue), the little tot's troubles had begun when his father had died twelve months earlier.

"Mr Morris came to the district about eighteen months ago," she said, "and eventually found a room in Beth's lodging house, a terraced building in a dismal court off Acton Street." The local street gossip had also revealed that, after a works accident which had killed his wife, he had decided to leave his native town of Hereford to find work in Manchester, where he hoped to build a future for himself and his small son. Unfortunately, the severe damp and harsh winter took its toll on a father who had struggled with bad health ever since arriving in the city and, when his death occurred in the springtime, there were few who showed surprise and even fewer who expressed concern for little Austin.

For months, Austin's pale and ragged form had been observed in and around the streets off London Road, a beer jug often in one hand whilst begging with the other. "Two weeks ago," explained Mrs Pritchard, "a young girl, one of several who are employed as 'street ladies' and entertain gentlemen friends at the house, called unexpectedly at her dwelling and begged her to find a way of removing Austin from the lodging house before it was too late." The girl, we learned, a frightened creature herself, let it be known that, since the father had died, young Austin had been employed by the women and girls to fetch beer from the public houses and he was fast becoming a skivvy for everyone who lodged at the house. His only comfort, the girl explained, was a corner cupboard in a downstairs room where Austin had salvaged old newspapers and a dirty blanket to fashion a makeshift bed and a hiding place. Of late, the demands on little Austin had become excessive and his already bruised body was beginning to show even further evidence of prolonged ill treatment. Before making a hurried departure the girl had left a bible with Mrs Pritchard, a keepsake which had been left by Mr Morris.

The same bible, a memento in safe keeping at the orphanage together with Mrs Pritchard's revelations, were now a part of the past. Even the article written by Gilbert Kirlew in reference to Austin, quoting the biblical story of the mother and her outcast boy in Beersheba, was fast fading from memory. "God heard the cry of help," Mr Kirlew had said in his summary, and in his usual biographical explanation in the monthly 'Cry of the Children', went on to illustrate how the motherless and fatherless Austin had been saved from the workhouse and the streets of Manchester —

"I think in little children God is best,
The best to love, and kind to know,
They come, and he is then our gentle guest,
And when they leave, all goodness seems to go.

In their small hands they bring a healing power,
Their frolic laugh will chase the darkest pain,
With so much warmth they fill the angel-hour,
That our chilled hearts must need unbend again."

"The closing hours of Whit Monday" — so read Leonard Shaw's report of the Whitsuntide holiday — "were spent at the Refuge, Strangeways, and in good time our sailor boys bid farewell to their old Manchester friends, and returned to the ship, leaving behind the recollections of a very happy day, a day which had started with the usual free breakfast provided by Mr Parker of Parker's restaurant in Market Street.

Wednesday — The lorries, kindly lent by Messrs Cross, Bleachers of Bolton, were at the Refuge door at one o'clock, and bore away some two hundred of our boys and children to Brooklands, Prestwich, where Mr William McConnell has now for several years invited them and shown much kindness. The beautiful fields adjoining the house never looked more lovely than on this occasion. Mr John W McConnell and his sisters were presently doing all they could to add to the enjoyments of their numerous little guests.

Thursday — Mr Walter Joynson, of Sale, had very kindly invited the large family from the Strangeways Refuge to visit his place on this day, which was reached by rail before three o'clock. A very enjoyable afternoon tea was provided, with much kindness shown by Mr Joynson.

Friday — was the all day trip, on the principle of keeping the best for the last. At an early hour our boys were on their way to Blackpool, to get a good big 'sniff of the briny' and a paddle in the sea. This is the great day of the week. Blackpool may be full of shops and shows and all kinds of attractions, but our boys are down at the shore — that is the attraction for them. A most enjoyable day was spent. Indeed, the whole week was one of much happiness and innocent enjoyment to the boys and girls connected with the large institution at Strangeways. Much of this is due to the admirable arrangements made by Gilbert Kirlew and Walter Browne the master, who was, as usual, unwearied in his efforts to keep everything right to make everybody happy.

Saturday — Was a quiet day at the Refuge and the various Homes, but not so at the outdoor branch of our work. It was specially devoted to the News Brigade and Caxton Brigade, who went to Alderley Edge and spent a very enjoyable day in Mr Jardine's grounds and rambling on the Edge. All expenses were borne by Mr Jardine and tea was provided by Mr Thomas Collier, and to both gentlemen the committee are much indebted."

Whilst reading through Kilby's notes in connection with the childrens' holiday, along with various other items of information intended for publication, I was suddenly reminded and aware of the fact that tomorrow was Sunday, a day which over the past few weeks had been pencilled into every Refuge committee member's diary. Speaking for myself, this special Sunday, as written and underlined in my own memo, proclaimed a day which, in my own opinion, was going to be momentous in the history of the Society and most certainly a red letter day for the Mothers at the Cheetham Orphan Homes:-

"Sunday 20th May, Leonard K Shaw will announce the names of the twelve boys who have been specially chosen to go to America as young disciples of Mr Moody."

Looking back on that unique and exciting chapter which was to change the lives of twelve of the Refuge children, I now pondered on the sequence of events which was to proclaim the return of the great American evangelist to Manchester.

'Moody and Sankey'
"We doubt not our readers have rejoiced at the prospect, now

generally known, of once more meeting our two American brethren, whose previous visit some years ago left its impressions on the citizens of Manchester. On the first day in March the two evangelists will commence a 15 day mission when meetings will be held at the YMCA, Free Trade Hall, Chepstow Street Circus, etc."

With some weeks to go before the much awaited arrival of Dwight Moody, the Refuge 'Monthly', in a similar explanation to that of its counterparts, gave this news to their readers in the February edition of the Christian Worker. Similarly, one month later, the March edition informed the public of the latest progress of Mr Moody and of his impending visit to the city. "We need hardly remind our readers that the brief mission of the famous American evangelist to our city begins on March 1st."

All too quickly Dwight Moody's visit to Manchester had ended and the committee, in a farewell gathering on the platform of Victoria Station, watched with mixed feelings as the noon day train to Leeds pulled away on its journey, taking the two Americans to their Yorkshire destination. Mr Moody's departure on what had been termed his 'Easter Mission' had left me with an emptiness and sadness of heart, and yet there were several good reasons why, like the vast majority of Mancestrians, I should be celebrating the rich legacies left behind. Kilby for one, in his admiration for his American friends, wasted little time in presenting his glowing verdict on the recent mission and, in the Easter edition of the Refuge journal, proclaimed its overwhelming success — "D L Moody in Manchester"

"For 14 days Manchester has once more been privileged to hear a voice which has borne God's message to so many hearts, the wide world over. There must have been many, in the vast audiences, perhaps the largest ever addressed in our city, who remembered that message coming home to them through the same lips nine years ago. It was a magnificent sight to see the impressive Free Trade Hall filled three times daily, crowded to overflowing each night, and to know the attraction which brought these multitudes together was the simple gospel of Christ. Thank God it is still 'the power of God unto salvation', as many a person found in that hall these past fourteen days. Each night men and women rose all over the hall and responded to Dwight Moody's appeal and each night the enquiry room was full to capacity. May they be, in His hand, a mighty power for the good of Manchester."

"The days and evenings were soon over, but it will take all eternity to finish their work. Mr Moody spoke with his old simple downright earnestness and American quaintness, and his old happy knack of translating Bible stories into living narratives of every day."

Whilst informing his readers of the obvious success of those two weeks in March and his subsequent meeting with the great man himself, Kilby offered a fragment of information to slip on to the back page, a sort of 'hors d'oeuvre' to the main feature he had prepared for the next edition.

"Mr Moody's early morning services were to our mind the most enjoyable of all. On last Sunday, 12th March, we took about 20 of our orphan boys, starting at seven o'clock am, from the George Street Homes in Cheetham Hill. Our three mile walk down to Manchester Cathedral was very pleasant, singing Sankey's hymns all the way. John Caton and George Woodhouse led the chorus 'We're marching to Canaan' which seemed very appropriate." As a participant of that eight o'clock service at which Mr Moody and Mr Sankey had inspired a large congregation, an occasion still clear in my mind, there had been a particular reference to Angels, a subject which had arisen as a result of Mr Moody's learning of the city's Angel Stone, housed in the cathedral. In his address, Mr Moody had compared the sandstone art work from the Collyhurst quarry to the rough diamonds of Angel Meadow and its vicinity.

Easter Sunday in '83, wintry, cold and with a tendency to snow, had arrived earlier than usual; on the 25th March I believe. Looking back to that vibrant and happy day I doubt whether any weather conditions could have penetrated the euphoria circulating amongst the committee and officials of the Refuges.

In the knowledge of certain circumstances which had resulted in good fortune descending on the Society, such news as £600 being received from Mr Studd of Sam's Chop House in Market Street for the purpose of emigrating street urchins, and bequests from certain well-to-do ladies towards the new Lytham Children's Holiday Home, had indeed set the stage for future optimism. After a busy day which had involved the Cheetham Orphan Homes and St John's Church, a short visit to Charter Street Ragged School and a final service at Frances Street, Leonard Shaw made a request to those officials and friends who were able to attend an informal meeting during that evening, when some "good news" in connection with the society would be revealed. That news, I pondered, was the very reason why I was now here in Northfield and Mount Hermon, an episode which had taken root.... Putting an immediate stop to my train of thought I returned to the Strangeways Homes and sat with the remainder of the assembly, wide-eyed and with a feeling of anticipation for the important announcement.

"Amongst the many good works in which Mr Moody is engaged," said Kilby in his usual quiet spoken voice, "is a training school for missionaries and evangelists, situated near his own home at Northfield, Massachusetts, in the United States. This is in connection with a farm of some four hundred acres and his plan is, while the young people are at school in training for future mission work, they should also be helping in the various operations of the farm, and thus gaining that physical strength and manly vigour without which they cannot do their lifes' work really well.

While Dwight Moody was engaged in his powerful mission to Manchester, the good work carried on at the Cheetham Orphan Homes in connection with the Boys' and Girls' Refuges, Strangeways, was brought to his attention and, having seen the orphan contingent at one of the early morning Sunday services, accepted the offer to visit the George Street Homes.

As a result of that visit to Cheetham, he has made an

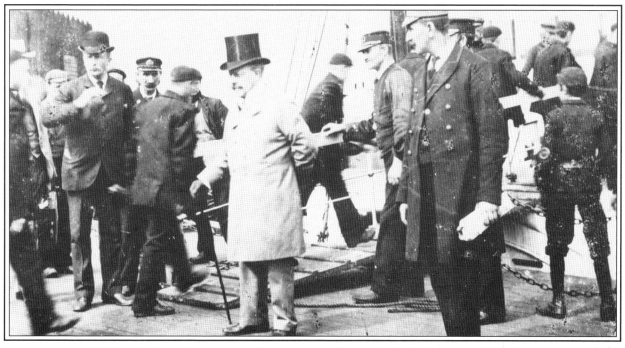

Dr Barnardo at Liverpool, escorting one of his emigrant party of boys to Canada. Kind permission of Barnardos.

offer to take twelve boys into his school at Mount Hermon, and then as many as show fitness and capacity for missionary work will, in due time, make application to one of the colleges. From there, the disciples will be sent forth as scripture readers, evangelists or missionaries, to labour in the noblest and happiest calling which can fall to any human lot.

This sudden and totally unexpected offer by Mr Moody came as a complete surprise and we only trust and assume that the Lord's hand was in it. Within the days to come, we on the committee will be actively engaged in selecting those twelve who, so far as we can see at the present, show the requisite disciple qualities of head and heart so essential for their future calling.

We ask for the prayers of this audience and of God's people that we may be guided in our choice and selection. That any of those who were rescued in early life by means of our Institution should become, in after years, Scripture readers and ministers of the gospel of our Lord, is an honour put upon our work in Manchester far beyond our fondest hopes. To God be all the glory. This is yet another illustration that "He chooses the weak things of this world to confuse those that are deemed to be mighty".

Concluding his speech, Kilby went on; "It is expected that the 'Twelve' will sail on or about the 1st of June."

About two weeks after that announcement the committee had met at Strangeways for their monthly council meeting, a gathering which had included a guest speaker, an acknowledged authority on child emigration. Mr Busk, a one time helper of the Liverpool Sheltering Homes and now an Inspector for the Canadian Immigration Council, showed his delight and approval when the news was given

to him concerning Mr Moody and the 'Twelve'. However, his visit to the Manchester society was to promote the emigration programme and to urge the committee to send out more boys for the Canadian farmers and even more girls for the farm homesteads. "Better still," he had said, "why not take a farm in Canada for the purpose of training boys at that end instead of Manchester, making the costs cheaper, and a great deal more satisfactory?"

By way of gaining support for his idea, Mr C W Busk produced a sheaf of papers from his bag and passed them among the committee members explaining that the extract was from a letter written by Lord Archibald Campbell, brother of the Marquis of Lorne, and received by the Canadian society:-

"Lord Lorne, the present Governor-General of Canada, may surely by this time be allowed to be a judge of the capabilities of Canada, and most decidely would not so enthusiastically love the land and its people, or long for the continual inroad of his fellow countrymen, did he really and truly believe that by doing so they would lay in the corner stone of their future success. Before many years have flown, the Government of this country will have to purchase probably whole regions as a refuge for the destitute in order to prevent actual starvation, and give thousands the chance of gaining a livelihood in 'Greater Britain'. Vast tracts of rich soil do not exist for nothing, and those who have seen these lands of the Far West and do not advocate emigration must be worse that fools. 'All day long, often', my brother told me, when journeying towards the Rockies, 'he wondered why no inhabitants were there,' so rich and lovely was the land they passed through. I refer to the Governor General of Canada's journey of last year."

As the meeting progressed I had become lost in my own thoughts. The two great emigration months were almost upon us and the orphans of the springtime would shortly be massing for that highway across the Atlantic. "Doctor Barnardo himself, would be personally escorting, for the very first time, one of his large contingents to Canada, and, although this journey was planned to take place the following year, preparations were well in hand to prepare the British Colony for thousands more of the Kingdom's 'little wanderers'." This information by Mr Busk reminded me of two recent incidents concerning Dr Barnardo and the Refuges, episodes which had caused me to question yet again the wisdom of child emigration.

The first event centred on 10 boys at the Strangeways Homes who had been accepted for the Barnardo party and who were due to sail in a few weeks' time. After journeying from Manchester to London to take up their short period of residence, the society was shocked, almost to embarrassment, when the same party was returned very late at night as being medically unsuitable, a situation which not only devastated the committee but caused Dr Boutflower to reaffirm his diagnosis of the boys' health as being perfectly in keeping with the emigration requirements.

This unsavoury episode was one of the reasons why Kilby had paid Dr Barnardo a visit during one of the East End conferences in London, and it was from this meeting that the second incident arose. Concerned at the large numbers of boys who were absconding whilst employed on the Canadian farms, Dr Barnardo had revealed an idea which was aimed at preventing the worsening of the situation. In short, Dr Barnardo gave his seal of approval to the new so called 'four year charter'. "By this method," Dr Barnardo had said, "the Manchester boys will receive a presentation of a silver watch if any of them keep the same situation for a period of not less than four years." In my affection for Kilby I had given my consent to Barnardo's methods but deep down I was conscious of my conflicting thoughts surrounding an idea which put a value on four of the most important years of adolescence.

Sunday 20th May
The all important day had finally arrived and the atmosphere in the Atkinson Home seemed to come alive as the committee members and friends were ushered into the building. First one boy entered the room and then another, until the whole group was positioned into two straight lines facing the audience. There was no mistaking the proud and happy looks on the faces of the twelve boys, and their clean appearance seemed to emphasise the youthful, if not angelic, innocence of a young band of would-be apostles. Rumours and gossip in connection with the twelve boys to be selected had been rife for some weeks, and, whilst the policy of Leonard Shaw and the committee had been one of secrecy so far as naming the 'twelve' was concerned, I was grateful that the moment had at last presented itself.

Apart from the group of boys themselves, the names of the selected 'twelve' had been known to the majority of the staff for almost four weeks but, as Kilby had said, "In fairness to the other children, the 'twelve' will not be informed until 10 days before the actual day of departure". The wisdom behind that statement was aimed at protecting the feelings of all the orphan children and to preserve the harmony throughout the Homes, a gesture which received the approval of all concerned.

Returning for a moment to the concluding chapter of Mr Moody's mission to Britain, I myself had been in Liverpool to catch a last opportunity to see and hear the evangelist before he set sail for his native America and it was here on the Monday evening of 16th April on the platform at Lime Street Station, that Kilby, arriving in the city to witness Moody's farewell meeting, told me that the unanimous decision had been reached. "I have with me the names of the twelve boys who have been chosen to go to America as disciples of Mr Moody and, if it is possible, I will hand him the list before he sets sail." In fact, Dwight Moody's departure did not occur until Saturday the 28th April, when he set sail aboard the Steamship 'Alaska' having, according to Kilby, officiated at several important functions, one of which was the formation of the Liverpool Society for the Prevention of Cruelty to Children.

"Since our American brethren have left us," wrote Kilby in his summing up of Moody and Sankey, "Liverpool has been the scene of gatherings as remarkable as those which took place during their short visit to Manchester. It was our privilege to be present at Hengler's Circus on Monday evening and, whether we consider the numbers present — between 6,000 and 7,000 — the singing, or the powerful address, the whole scene was a most impressive one, and will not soon pass from memory.

By 6.30 pm every inch of space had been taken, with overflow meetings taking place at Emmanuel Church and at College Hall. Gallery on gallery in every conceivable place, right up to the roof of the building, all closely packed with earnest faces — and all looking one way. After the preliminary speeches given by Mr Menzies and Professor Drummond of Glasgow, Mr Moody delivered a most powerful message to the masses of Liverpool...."

'The Diary', a personal collection of letters, newspaper cuttings and other information concerning the Twelve, had been included amongst my private possessions for the American excursion. Ever since Mr Moody had departed from Manchester, I had taken to accumulating whatever news came my way where the Manchester boys were concerned. Theirs was such an inspiring and successful story that thumbing the pages of the diary had not only become a habit, but more of a stimulation. Right from the beginning the fairy tale qualities had fired my imagination, proving that not only did good triumph over evil, but that from little acorns oak trees grew. Trying hard to dismiss momentarily the fate of two of those saplings, I turned to my diary and began once again to trace the story of the Twelve, a chronicle which I had prefixed: 'Angels from a Manchester Meadow'.

Monday April 23rd, 1883 St George's Day. (Extract from Refuge Magazine)
"Our last number alluded to the offer of Mr Moody to receive twelve of the boys of the Orphan Homes into his Training Home and Farm School, at Mount Hermon, Massachusetts, there to be trained for Mission work in the great Western continent. It will interest many of our readers to learn that twelve very hopeful boys have been chosen, and that the party sails on Wednesday, May 30th, in the steamship 'Cephalonia', for their new home in America. The committee of the Strangeways institution naturally view the experiment, for such it must be regarded at present, with much interest. They feel that it is the highest honour ever put upon their work, and they desire to thank God that amongst their boys have been found those whose future rests in this connection. But they rejoice with trembling, and would very earnestly ask the prayers of the Lord's people on the undertaking. Let all unite in asking Him in whose name and for whose sake the whole matter has been undertaken, to go with the little disciples on the 30th and give them that special fitness which He alone can give — in a word, Bless them, and Make them Blessings, wherever their lot may be cast.

Note, many friends are taking an interest in this undertaking and are showing that interest in a practical way, amongst whom we would mention the Kersal Ladies' Sewing Party, who are providing the outfit of day shirts for the 'twelve'."

April 24th
"Leonard Shaw confirmed that, as a result of his visit to Liverpool Docks on the 17th, he has obtained the passages for the Twelve at reduced terms."

April 25th
"Mrs Marchant of 105 Fairfield Road, Droylsden, called at the offices at Strangeways today to give her approval and consent to the emigration of her two grandsons, Frederick and Benjamin Platt. Doctor Boutflower stated that, along with the remainder of the Twelve, her two boys were in excellent health."

Within the spaces and blank pages prior to the Whit Week diary of events, I had pencilled the names of the twelve orphans who had been named as the finalists to go to Mr Moody's school, a selection which, according to Kilby, had been very thorough and painstaking."
1. Frank Critchlow
2. John Raynes
3. John Collings Caton
4. Edwin Albert Cartledge
5. George Woodhouse
6. Alfred Beasley
7. Frederick Marchant Platt
8. Benjamin Marchant Platt
9. Walter Walker
10. Joseph Dooley
11. George Tobin
12. Austin Charles William Morris

Wednesday May 9th
"Leonard Shaw and the committee were very disturbed on reading an article in the Manchester Evening News under the title — 'Pauper Emigration to the United States'.

"The governor of Massachusetts wrote, protesting at the landing of pauper children at Boston, and said he would use America's diplomatic powers to prevent paupers from England being shipped over. He said he would refer the matter to President Arthur."

Thursday, May 10th
"Mrs Birt of the Liverpool Sheltering Homes paid a brief visit to the Strangeways Institution to collect details of the girls who are emigrating to Canada."

With a return to the 'declaration', an expression I had chosen in conjuction with the revelation of the twelve names, I was able to recapture from my notes the warmth and satisfaction which had emanated from the shy and awkward young boys. The words, spoken first by Leonard Shaw and then Gilbert Kirlew, had fallen on very serious faces, especially during the declaration of their fate as 'chosen disciples'. Only later did the boys begin to appreciate the good fortune which had descended on them, when hearing the congratulatory comments from the wives of committee members.

Being the eldest, Frank Critchlow and John Raynes had been singled out as the two leaders of the group or, as Mr Browne had suggested, in apostolic terms, "the Luke and Paul of the Twelve". This remark by the bearded and handsome Walter Browne caused me to reflect for a moment and ponder on the assimilation of the remainder of the flock. John Caton, now with a relaxed smile and carrying on a light hearted conversation with his friends, was in my opinion the 'Peter' of the group, whilst the more serious looking George Woodhouse compared favourably with 'John'. One by one I searched the faces of the boys and in my mind's eye apportioned the qualities of each of them to those of the New Testament heroes.

Monday 21st May
"Confirmation arrived today with regard to the sailing of the 'Cephalonia' on the 30th."

Tuesday 22nd May
"Mr and Mrs Shaw named the six girls of the Cheetham Orphanage who have been selected to go to Canada with Maria Rye's party. As in the case of the Twelve, they will sail from Liverpool on the 30th in the steamship 'Sardinia'."

1. Anne Fleming
2. Alice Campbell
3. Annie Doyle
4. Hannah Launders
5. Rachael Launders
6. Priscilla Gorrall

Friday 25th May
"Mr Napper, a teacher at St John's School in Cheetham, gave an evening talk to the twelve boys on current affairs. Included in his lecture was a reference to the recent spate of typhoons, cyclones and tornadoes which had been sweeping across the Western States of America."

Saturday 26th May
"Some of the George Street boys and girls attended the opening of the Bignor Street 'Hightown Bowling Green', at which the Refuges Band performed.

'Farewell Tea Party — 6.30 pm...'"
I remembered thinking at this particular time how the weeks had become days and the hours, precious moments in which to savour the infectious excitement. Within this atmosphere of overwhelming jubilation the committee and wives assembled for what was to be the highlight of all their efforts. Other guests and friends included the philanthropic public who had played some part in providing whatever was necessary towards the outfits and passages of the Twelve. One of these, a close friend of Leonard Shaw's, was Mr A G Higgins, a Manchester man who had supported the Refuge on many occasions. Because of its lengthy description and accuracy, his was the version of accounts concerning the boy's departure selected for publication in the Refuge journal, and once again I turned the well thumbed pages of my diary to recall those former days in Manchester.

"Our readers will remember that in our last number we announced that the twelve boys in connection with the Cheetham Orphan Homes who were to join Mr Moody in America had been chosen. A busy time has been spent since then in preparing their outfit, and making general arrangements for their departure.

On Saturday evening May 26th, a most interesting tea party was held at the Homes and at 6.30pm a large number of friends, with as many of the boys and girls as could find room, sat down together to tea in No. 4 Home. Although Saturday evening was naturally an inconvenient time for ministers, many had most kindly accepted the invitation in order to show their sympathy and interest.

After tea there was a general adjournment to one of the other houses, where the rest of the evening was happily spent in a quiet, earnest meeting. It was opened by a prayer from the Rev. C G K Gillespie:

'Dear Friends, pray for our children, and especially the twelve boys who are about to embark upon their journey to the great American continent! Money is useful, personal help is useful; the thoughtful gifts we receive from time to time are useful; but prayer! prayer which moves the hand that moves the world, is more useful than all else. Pray for our children, for the few that leave us, that in their new home in a distant land they may never disgrace the Homes they have left; — for the many that remain with us, that they may be preserved from the temptations of the city, and growing up in the fear of God, become a blessing and not a curse, a strength and not a weakness, to the land of their birth! And some day you shall know the full meaning of the words, in as much as ye have done it unto one of the least of these, ye have done it unto me.'

Afterwards, everyone in the room joined together in the great and most appropriate hymn, 'Guide us Oh thou Great Jehovah'. We wish our space would permit us to insert some account of the striking and very moving address from our various friends, which we trust our boys will never forget. Mr Kirlew, having to leave early, was the first to speak, and he was followed by the Rev. Maltby, W Young, Prebendary MacDonald, G G K Gillespie, Mr T W Freston, L K Shaw, and Mr Napper, to the latter of whom our boys owe so much for his excellent teaching in St John's School.

The greatest kindness has been shown to the dear lads themselves and, at the conclusion of a tearful and joyful evening, many friends gathered round to give them a parting handshake and to wish them God-speed. We trust and believe that they will prove worthy of all the goodness shown to them and that God will indeed go with them and bless them wherever their lot may be cast.

The usual noon-day business-men's prayer meeting at the YMCA on the following Tuesday was of such a special character. Our little band of disciples was present on this occasion, and once more we joined in committing them and our beloved friends, Mr and Mrs Shaw, who will accompany them, to the safe keeping of Our Father in Heaven. The room was crowded, and it rejoiced our hearts to see the deep interest and sympathy manifested by all. It was indeed a hallowed moment, and we could not doubt that the Master was present to answer the fervent prayers offered by so many hearts. The chair was taken by the Rev. Prebendary MacDonald, always a firm supporter of our work amongst children; whilst a few loving words of counsel and prayer were also spoken by the Revs. Parkinson, Henry Bone and W Young. The tone of the meeting may be gathered from the beautiful remark made to Mr Shaw by a lady at its close — "I'm sure that the ship in which they are to sail must be safe, for it is freighted with so many prayers."

There seemed indeed but a few dry eyes in the room even among those who were comparative strangers, for we could not but think of the parting which was almost imminent. And as we looked on the bright and bonny twelve lads before us, our hearts ached, especially for the dear Mothers of our Homes, who loved those boys almost as their own children, and to whom the grief of losing them is perhaps more than anyone will ever know. They will leave a sad vacuum behind them and amid the uncertainties of life we know it is very doubtful if we will ever meet again on earth. Yet we send forth the Twelve thankfully, to be used in the Master's service and, as we trust, to be instruments in His hands in leading many to righteousness. Nor should we forget to pray that the rest and change of this voyage may be of much benefit to our dear Leonard Shaw and his wife, and that they may return to us strengthened and refreshed for the work to which they have consecrated their lives."

My recollection of that last meeting in the 'Moody' room of the YMCA, a gathering reminiscent almost of the biblical 'last supper', had been a very moving experience. Reflecting on that statement I had made to Kilby regarding the freighted ship and its cargo was now reason enough for me to escape the Northfield tragedy and dwell for a moment on the happier times. After the breaking of the bread and partaking of the wine, each boy received a personal handshake and a 'God Speed' from Prebendary MacDonald, a gesture which was repeated by every one of the invited guests.

Mr Shaw and Mr Newett were amongst the last to offer the handshake of farewell and like myself had watched from a distance as the solemn ceremony developed into an emotional drama. It had not been a gloom and doom meeting nor one of ecstatic jubilation, but rather one where the mingling of emotions and spirit had been in complete harmony. To me personally, that harmonisation had produced the most rewarding and uplifting sensation I had ever experienced, especially during the singing of the Lord's Prayer. Never before had I heard it so beautifully rendered and, as the harmony of young soprano and male baritone reached its peak, I became immersed in an experience which produced a flood of spiritual tears. That the hand of God had been in it was beyond my discernment, and yet it was obvious that witness had been made of a most unusual happening.

Wednesday 30th May
Departure of the Twelve
I arrived at the Central Station in good time to join the small group of well wishers and observed from the station clock that forty-five minutes remained before the departure of the Liverpool-bound train. I decided to take advantage of the late morning sunshine, occupying a vantage point opposite the fruit and vegetable stalls. From this location on the corner of Mount Street I was ideally situated to observe the boys as they approached Central Station from the Albert Square.

According to Kilby the Twelve had been invited by the Lord Mayor to the Town Hall, where they were to receive a new shilling and a 'bon voyage'. Within ten minutes Mr and Mrs Shaw led the party across the busy thoroughfare of Peter Street and judging by the noisy chatter and the smil-

ing faces they were already full of the day's excitement. The luggage belonging to Leonard Shaw and the boys was already stacked in a neat pile on the station platform, a task which had been performed by the boys of the Refuge Industrial Brigade.

Under Mr Browne's direction the uniformed boys of the Shoe Blacks and Messenger Brigade helped in the distribution of the luggage, whilst offering handshakes and a last farewell to their comrades. The smartness of the boys, the overall neatness, and the contrasting fashion attire, proved sufficient reason for fellow travellers and passers-by to turn their heads. For Kilby's sake, I was proud with the results, proud for all those friends and helpers at the orphanage who had produced the clothes and, more than anything else, proud of the twelve boys who now contrasted so vividly with their former ragged appearance. Thankfully, Kilby had very wisely invited his friend and associate Mr Broughton to the George Street Orphan Homes to photograph the twelve boys prior to their departure. Turning a page of the Diary, I now reflected on the photograph which had proved to be one of great value to the Refuges. This personal memento, which I had captioned: "From Manchester to Massachusetts — The Twelve Boy Disciples", captured Leonard Shaw and the twelve boys in a relaxed pose on the doorsteps of No. 2 Home. Six of the boys were wearing the Scots bonnets, perhaps the most popular head-dress adopted by the emigrant children, whilst the remainder apart from Austin Morris, had preferred the more mature bowler hat. Little Austin, I was to learn later, had been very reluctant to part with his favourite American military style cap and Kilby had allowed him to wear it for the journey.

At 2.15pm precisely, the carriage doors opened onto the platform of Lime Street Station in Liverpool. The scenic journey from Manchester had only taken an hour and thanks to my travelling companion Mr Kirlew, the task of occupying the boys' minds had been easy, with his conversation in matters of general knowledge.

I was particularly impressed by the revelations in regard to the 'Cephalonia', the ship in which the boys were sailing. According to Gilbert Kirlew, the Cephalonia had been launched only twelve months since, on the river Mersey, and at the time was the largest ship ever to be built at Birkenhead. "It was coincidental", said Mr Kirlew, "that nine months earlier, the Cephalonia had sailed to Boston in America on its maiden voyage, and today's sailing was, as far as he was aware, the first one to the United States since returning from Australasia." Another of Mr Kirlew's disclosures was in reference to the Tsar of Russia, a topic which for a short while had held his young audience captive. "Today, for the first time, the new Emperor and Empress will take their seats at the St Andrew's Hall in the Kremlin Palace of Moscow." This news item, simply explained by Mr Kirlew, continued further as he described in detail the pomp and pageantry of the coronation of Alexander the third of Russia, the new Tsar. By the time the Mersey-based 'Indefatigable' training ship had entered into conversation the train was drawing into the station and the eager-faced boys, like little mariners, were

Leonard R. Shaw and his TWELVE, photographed at the Orphan Homes, George Street, Cheetham Hill. 30th May 1883.

becoming responsive to the call of the sea.

Kilby had once remarked that Liverpool and Manchester were almost identical except for one obvious trait, manifested by the westerly winds. I could now detect that salty tang which Kilby had referred to and, though the afternoon was sunny and the sky cloudless, the strong breezes on Lime Street bore all the indications of an incoming tide. Mrs Birt's appearance at the station had been a relief to Kilby, especially when she introduced the handful of boys from the Myrtle Street Homes. Walking in formation to the dockside with the eager help of the volunteer luggage carriers, the emigrant party attracted the stares of the city workers, some of whom, after glancing at the luggage labels bearing the Boston and Massachusetts destination, offered a bon voyage.

The sights and sounds of the quayside of Alexander Dock on a day when I came face to face with the world of emigration has never receded from memory, and probably never will. Hundreds of people in stages of either immigration or emigration swarmed along the quayside, whilst a further population idled in the warm sunshine of early summer. Making our way through the obstacles of varying bundles of baggage, one could sense the urgency of the sea-going fraternity, all endeavouring to be ready for the turn of the tide. Numerous groups of people, including the eminent ladies and gentlemen down to the poor in their flat caps and shawls, stood around in groups, some with smiling looks and others with forlorn expressions of apprehension. The steady march of the boys had now steadied to a slow rhythm as we made our way to a terminal by a large storage warehouse where the Rev. Lundie and Mr Carter, the teacher from the Indefatigable Training Ship, had arranged a rendezvous.

Perhaps it was the sight of so many young children, mainly girls, which drew my attention, or possibly it was the recognition of Maria Rye. Whatever the reason, I felt that the journey so far as I was concerned had finally come to an end. Whilst the appearance of the children on the quay demanded admiration and congratulations, I became saddened and concerned as I observed the scores of childish faces, all lined up and awaiting the command to depart from their homeland. Just as I began to feel the pangs of apprehension for the little emigrants, a shout from Benjie Platt and Joseph Dooley indicated that a friend from the Manchester Homes had been spotted. In fact, the friend and acquaintance turned out to be the six girls from the George Street Orphanage and who were now a part of Miss Rye's Canadian emigration party.

By now the rest of the boys had begun an exchange of conversation with their former school friends and, whilst the boys were proudly showing off their new suits, I noticed the large labels pinned to the coat lapels of all the girls. Little Ann Fleming and Alice Doyle, whose faces I recognised, were holding hands and attempting to exchange stories, whilst Hannah and Rachael Launders offered much bolder conversation, even to the point of using the more familiar

The 'CEPHALONIA' on which the TWELVE sailed to BOSTON, USA in 1883. By kind permission of the Williamson Art Gallery Museum, Birkenhead.

nicknames of the Twelve. Directing my attention to the labels, particularly the one worn by Annie Doyle, I read:- 'Our Western Home, Niagara, Ontario — Miss Rye, SS Sardinia'. Presumably the other large group of children further along the quayside, about a hundred or so, was Mrs Birt's emigrant party whose ranks included some Manchester waifs. In fact it occured to me at that moment that, by early evening, three of the ships leaving the Mersey would have a representation of Manchester Refuge Children on board.

Suddenly, the day was over and as, according to the words of that beautiful hymn, the night time drew nigh, the evening shadows flitting across a setting sun became images and reflections of my thoughts. That was the last I had seen of the Twelve until the present time and, although my heart had been heavy with loss at the Liverpool terminal, the task had been made comparatively easy, mainly through the cheerfulness of the whole group. Before stepping on to the tender, I had shaken the hand of every boy, a gesture which included both a prayer and a last minute reminder that Manchester was proud of its disciples and would watch with interest the progress of its twelve young sons.

Pausing at the Albert Dock quay on my way to Mrs Birt's Sheltering Home, I turned for a last view of the ship's lights in the far distance. Somewhere at the back of my mind amidst the turmoil of the day was a particular verse whose author and origin I had long since forgotten but whose moving words seemed strangely appropriate:-

'How the children leave us,
and no traces linger of that smiling Angel band;
Gone! forever gone! and in their places
Weary men and anxious women stand.'

True to their promises the boys, especially Johnnie Raynes, Frank Critchlow and John Caton, all wrote regularly to the Strangeways Homes, whilst Kilby took great delight in informing the committee of their experiences at Northfield. In his first newsletter to the readers of the Refuge magazine since returning from America, Leonard Shaw informed his audience of the success of his recent journey to Massachusetts and, under the column dedicated to the emigrated children entitled 'News from the West', made special reference to the splendid conduct of the Twelve during the crossing of the Atlantic.

Painful as it was at this time, I continued the chapter of events in my diary and relived the happy hours when the much read letters from America had been passed to me to add to the collection. The first and very imformative letter was from George Woodhouse:

'Mr Moody's School
Mount Hermon on the Hill
Northfield, Massachusetts.

Dear Mr and Mrs Browne
I thought you and the boys at Strangeways would like to know of our safe arrival at our new home in America.

After the bell rang for the tender to leave the Cephalonia, we all waved to Mr Kirlew and the others before setting sail. When we left Liverpool we came to New Brighton and soon after this we saw the lightship which is supposed to be the beginning of the Irish Sea. The next morning a steward knocked on the cabin doors and shouted "Seven o'clock gentlemen, fine morning and a fair wind", and these words were repeated every day until we reached Boston. When we went on deck we saw rows of lovely white cottages shining in the sun and the steward said we were coming into Cork harbour in Ireland. The scenery and the green hills behind Queenstown was so green that we could not believe our eyes. After the passengers had come on board we set sail once more for America. The last piece of land we saw was the Fastnet Rock with a lighthouse on it. The weather was very good during the voyage and we saw a whale as big as the Cephalonia.

From your true friend,
George Woodhouse.'

'Boys Home, Mount Hermon.

I feel very happy here, and I hope I may always keep so. The place where I live is a Boys' School, where farming and general studies is taught. It is situated on a mountain, and the scenery all round is very beautiful. We go to the Connecticut river to practice swimming and one day I ventured out too far, and should have been drowned had not John Caton, who can swim, caught hold of me and brought me to the side.

Your good friend,
Edwin Cartledge.'

'Mount Hermon School.

Dear Mother
I now take pleasure in writing to you. We go to Church on Sundays. Mr Moody preached and it was very enjoyable. We have about forty cows, two oxen, one bull, forty pigs, twelve calves, and twenty turkeys. Then Mrs Moody has two deer. We work hard amongst the hay and corn and are very happy.

Yours affectionately,
Alfred Beasley.'

'The Mount Hermon School.

Dear Mr and Mrs Shaw
I was so pleased to get your kind letter, and so was Johnnie and Frank. I am getting quite a farmer now. I can drive a horse, and I enjoy going to the woods. There are many nice things there, such as Indian arrow heads etc. And we have a large farm. It has 400 acres of land, plenty of cows, seven horses, two yoke of oxen, besides plenty of poultry. There

is going to be a convocation next week. We shall have a grand old time, and a holiday all week. I am thankful that I came here. I know that God has led me to this place. May God bless and prosper you in your work in Manchester.

Yours affectionately
John C Caton.'

'Mount Hermon on the Hill

Dear Mr Shaw
    I am sending my school report to you sir, so that you can sign your name, and then please return it to me. We have got a hymn about the school, called 'Mount Hermon is our Home'. We have had our bedrooms made nice. We have large spring beds and a bookcase over them. Our home is called 'The Manchester Home' because the twelve Manchester boys live there. Austin sleeps in the next bed and he sends his love to you and the homes of Cheetham. Please give my love to Mrs Shaw and Miss Higgins.

Your friend,
George Tobin.'

Mount Hermon, Northfield.

Dear Sir
    I had just returned from a lecture on California when your letter arrived. It was good to hear of your safe return to the old country and of the visit by Lord Shaftesbury to the Refuge Homes. Do you remember the incident on board ship when you were telling us the story of Jonah and when at that moment a big black whale appeared on the port side? You will be pleased to know that John Caton and Johnnie Raynes are joining with me to form an American branch of the BOK. I hope you enjoyed reading my description of Boston in my previous letter. The scenery here at Northfield is very beautiful and I, for one, thank God that I was chosen by Mr Moody to come here.
    May God bless you and Mrs Shaw at the Strangeways Mission.

Yours truly,
Frank Critchlow.'

'Mount Hermon on the Hill,
Northfield.

Dear Mr and Mrs Shaw
    I have some good news to tell you. Mr Boyd said we can play football and cricket when the time comes and I have been chosen to teach football to the American boys. The weather is very fine over here and I have been collecting the hay and corn with Mr Moody. Some of the others have been biten by big mosceetos but I escaped them.

Yours truly,
Joseph Dooley.'

Alfred Beesley at Mount Hermon in 1885.

CHAPTER TWELVE

utting pen to paper in a final attempt to conclude my letter to Manchester in England, a task which was causing mingling sensations of bitterness and resentment, I thought again of the grief it would cause at the Orphan Homes and of the ordeal which the committee would have to face...

Little Austin Morris and George Tobin are the two English boys and James Hill of Stamford, Connecticut, is the other of the trio. According to Frank Critchlow, the boys who stayed on at the school during vacation, those who do not have homes to go to — set off for an afternoon bathing session down at the river. It appears that George Tobin and James Hill, intent on reaching a sandbar out in the river, diverted from the main party to avoid detection. Neither of them could swim and, as they waded the 200 feet across the strong currents of the Connecticut, they began to sink, both of them crying for help. Little Austin Morris, the youngest of the group, was the first to throw off his jacket and dive to the rescue of his friends but, not being a swimmer, he too began to sink. Walter Walker and Joseph Dooley were the next to rush into the river followed by Johnnie Caton. In trying to reach the drowning boys, Joey went under twice, and was on the point of drowning himself; Walter went down once, but both managed to wade ashore. Johnnie Caton had by this time got to Austin, who was sinking for the third time, and managed to get a faint hold of him, when a Canadian boy, who had also gone to the rescue, came swimming by, and not knowing that Austin, who was under the water, was clinging hold of Johnnie, knocked him out of his grasp, and the little body sank. By the time Mr Moody's boat had taken to the water, Little Austin's body had been found, and a

few minutes later the other bodies were rescued by Louis Johnson, a Choctaw American Indian boy.

It was a most awfully sad day yesterday. The heat and the death by drowning made the burial most essential. At the school house it was so sad to see the caskets (coffins) with the three boys side by side.

I had made wreaths for them and the school had been decorated so prettily with white and pink flowers and the wild maiden hair. According to American custom, the top part of the coffin was left open, so that anyone could see the faces of the little fellows. A sister and brother, and a lady who had been interested in the American orphan boy, were present. They arrived from New York just before the funeral. The two English boys had no one to mourn for them. Mr Moody said at the funeral that his heart ached for them so, and he was so thankful that a Manchester lady was there. It is the first death they have experienced in connection with either Northfield or Mount Hermon School. It was so sad to see the little desks in the school house decorated with flowers, and even more painful at the sight of young Austin's peaked cap, placed on the desk top. To think that the three little fellows were sat behind those desks only yesterday.

The funeral procession moved so slowly along the lanes, the air heavy with sadness. First Mr D L Moody, then the three coffins, carried by the boys of the school; then an open carriage with the sister and brother of the American boy; then a waggon with Mrs Moody and the teachers; then my-self, in a buggy, and some other friends you would not know.

The little cemetery looked right over the Connecticut River, near to the graves of Mr Moody's family, on the Holton's side,

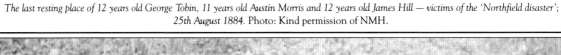

The last resting place of 12 years old George Tobin, 11 years old Austin Morris and 12 years old James Hill — victims of the 'Northfield disaster'; 25th August 1884. Photo: Kind permission of NMH.

for eight generations. The three boys were laid in a broad grave, side by side. The prospect from this place is simply lovely, but I have to admit that this was a very, very sad scene. The graveside service was conducted under a burning sun and a clear blue sky, the ministry being performed by Mr Moody, the Rev. George Pentecost and Rev. E R Drake. I have with me a flower taken from the coffins of the English boys, in case there is anyone in Manchester who cares for it. It was picked by Bennie Platt during my recital of a poem which had been a favourite of George and Austin at the Manchester Homes.

'Let the little children come
To a Saviour's breast;
Little souls feel weariness
Little hearts need rest.

Little saints have work to do,
Little souls to win,
Standing at the golden gate
Asking children in.

Heaven is full of little ones
God's great nursery
Where the faintest flower on earth
Bloom eternally.'

Standing at the graveside with the boys of the school, Mr and Mrs Dan Boyd, and some other staff members, we all sang 'Thy will be done' and everyone repeated the Lord's Prayer together. I think I have never heard it so beautifully portrayed. Tears were plentiful and flowed freely, especially among the younger of the Manchester boys who grieved intensely at the loss of their friends. Mr Moody is terribly cut up over the incident. Referring to the time when he welcomed those twelve boys from Manchester at Northfield station and drove them to his home, he told the gathering at this funeral how near God seemed to him, and how he felt they were chosen and sent to him by God.

Finally, Leonard, the true meaning of the text from John 15.13 — 'Greater love hath no-one than this, that he lay down his life for his friends' — was so relevant in the case of little Austin Morris. When this text was rendered I was so proud to have stood for him in his bravest and finest hour.

Please give my deepest sympathies to everyone at the Strangeways Home and a special heartfelt sympathies to the Mothers at the Cheetham Orphan Homes.

For you Leonard, knowing how despairing your thoughts must be at this hour, I think a verse from one of your favourite poems will offer a shred of comfort and a renewed sense of purpose:

'Twas only a deed of kindness,
perchance it was not seen;
A helping hand to a struggling friend,
not done to be seen of men.

But the Master watched with pleasure,
for the motive he could see;
And he said, as he smiled so sweetly,
'Ye have done it unto Me.'

As always, 'in Christ'.   Jane Newett.

EPILOGUE

On the 10th of September, 1884 a paragraph appeared in the monthly journal of the Refuges relating to 'an accident at Mount Hermon', a text which incorporated the black border of mourning ....

> "Just as we go to press, tidings of a sad calamity reaches us. Two of our boys at Mr Moody's school, at Northfield, USA — two of the bright, happy group whom we took out last year — were drowned on August 25th, in the Connecticut River, which flows near the school. One, George Tobin, was bathing, and got out of his depth; Austin Morris jumped in to try and save him and both were lost. We are greatly distressed and can only bow beneath His hand and say
>
> 'Thy will be done'
>
> Rescued from the depths here, they were growing up full of hope and promise there. We had heard of the accident to some boys ten days ago, but as no cable reached us we concluded that they could not be Manchester boys. We wait further details with anxiety, and hope to give them to our readers in our next issue."

The subsequent October issue presented the Mount Hermon episode as follows:

"DISASTER AT NORTHFIELD, USA

DEAR LITTLE HELPERS — I want to tell you this month of a Birth and then of a Death, and finally of a Work in which all who read these lines may take a share and help.

By a birth, I do not mean the actual birth of a baby into our world, but the entrance of a child into our Homes, for this, in many cases, is the beginning of a new life to them. Most of them do not know their birthdays and when they come to us, and as we always observe birthdays in our family homes, we give them a new birthday, generally the day they enter, which becomes ever after a very real birthday to them.

This was so in the case of bright faced little George Tobin, whose life up to the time of his coming to our Homes was a sad one. Father died a few years ago, and then Mother remarried, which was a bad day for George. It was poverty before, but it was, in addition, cruelty and neglect, and blows and curses from his stepfather, until little George's life became a burden instead of being a bright happy thing; and then, darkest day of all, mother died; the only one who cared for George, the one to shield him from the man who should have been a father to him, was gone, and the poor boy wished he were dead too.

A short time after this, a good woman was passing through one of our Manchester cemeteries when a child's sobs caught her ear. She naturally turned to see where they came from, and there sitting upon a grave close by was A Little Ragged boy, sobbing as though his heart would break. It was little George at his mother's grave!

The motherly heart who spoke to him found out that he was not only fatherless and motherless, but homeless — for George had left the man who had ill-used both himself and his mother until the day she died, when a kind neighbour gave him temporary shelter. This young woman did what we hope we would have done, dear young friends. She brought him to the Refuge in Strangeways, and soon little George was safe and happy in one of our Orphan Homes, where he is gradually forgetting the old life, gradually entering on the new.

"THIS IS THE BIRTH —

EIGHTEEN MONTHS AGO — a group of twelve happy boys were in the middle of the Atlantic Ocean aboard one of the splendid steam-ships of the Cunard line, which carry passengers from Liverpool to America. The weather was fine, the sea calm, and all sorts of games were going forward on deck, in which the boys joined, and they were so bright and happy, and obedient, that all the passengers liked them.

A lady and gentleman were taking the boys over to a large farm school in America, where a home had been offered to them by Mr Moody. These boys had been brought up in our Orphan Homes at Cheetham Hill and the 'mothers' who loved them there, gave them pretty little text books on leaving, and each morning the boys loved to come and repeat their text for the day:

THE YOUNGEST IN THE GROUP, was little Austin, aged 10 years, and one morning on going to his cabin, the gentleman found him busy learning the text, and putting his arm around him, asked him very earnestly and thoughtfully if he thought he was God's child? The large eyes filled with tears, which soon rolled down his face and rosy cheeks. The words had touched a tender cord in that little heart.

Kneeling down together in the little cabin, a few simple words of prayer were offered asking for the best of blessings for that dear fatherless and motherless boy. From that day forth, no brighter and happier face than Austin's was seen on board ship.

The voyage over, a good long railway journey on a bright summer's day brought the group of boys to their journey's end, where a hearty welcome awaited them.

Rather more than twelve months have passed away, and the boys are still at the Farm School, growing into healthy strong lads with the farm work, and learning all the time, when one summer day they go down to the river side: Austin is among them; two of the group have gone to bathe; the others are gathering mussels and flowers, when suddenly a cry is raised for help — THE TWO BOYS ARE DROWNING!"

In a moment one of those on the bank was seen throwing off his jacket and boots and plunging in to the rescue of his companions. Who is that brave boy? It is little Austin!

Bravely he dives and swims against the swiftness of the river, with splendid foolishness, matching the boy's strength against the cruel current.

A few yards from the sinking ones, little Austin succumbs, and all three are lost.

"THIS IS THE DEATH"

"A dark cloud, yes, but it has a silver lining — the memory of that morning in the cabin of the Cunard Steamer, 'Cephalonia' will never pass away. I know our young readers will share the joy at the Birth and also our sorrow at the Death."

Five years after the emigration of the Twelve, Mr Kirlew of the Strangeways Homes visited the farms in Ontario to see for himself the results of the Manchester Children's Emigration Scheme. Before returning to England he paid a visit to the Mount Hermon Boys' School at Northfield where he met and talked with the Manchester Boys. Extracts of information and conversation recorded in Gilbert Kirlew's diary, are as follows:-

"1888. One of the greatest joys of our American visit was to see the lads who five years ago were admitted to Mount Hermon College (Mr D L Moody's), no longer boys, but most of them young men, who we felt glad to own as sons and brothers.

"What do you mean to be?" I said to one, "Well," he replied, "first I want to be fit for something. I am well on in Greek now, and I'll be through my classical course in two years, and then I'm ready for the Lord's will."

"I'm taking music and singing specially Sir," replied George Woodhouse, "and I mean to use all I know in the Lord's service." So round the circle it went, most of the group giving clear and decided answers concerning their experience of pardoning grace. We then joined and in turn, asked a blessing on the dear old Refuge and Homes in Manchester, as well as upon the band of students working their way through one of the best colleges in the United States.

"Working their way through," we said, for it must not be forgotten that these young men are at manual work and labour a sufficient time each, to pay for their support, and like all other colleges in America, the tuition is free; but this freedom has been obtained in this instance from the generous friends on both sides of the Atlantic by the exertions of Mr D L Moody.

We had an abundance of messages from the young friends to their former acquaintants in the old country. "I want to come and help you at Strangeways when I am through here," said one of the students who knows from past experience what wickedness abounds us in Manchester.

Frank Critchlow, one of the first band who was sent from the Cheetham Homes to Mr Moody's school five years ago, will graduate this year, and he intends, if the way is open, to enter the Princeton University and then devote his life to God's service."

On July 15th, 1888, five students from Mr Moody's school arrived at Liverpool for the start of a four week working holiday in connection with the Strangeways Refuges, their visit being declared in the August edition of the 'Cry of the Children'....

"QUARTET CHOIR FROM MOUNT HERMON
COLLEGE, USA, IN MANCHESTER"
"The five young men whose visit we announced in our last issue have arrived, and a week's mission of a very interesting character, in connection with the Boy's and Girl's Refuge, Strangeways, was begun on Tuesday evening July 17th, in the schools of the Broughton Park Congregational Church, Cheetham Hill. The beautiful Gospel hymns very touchingly sung by the four well harmonised voices reached out to the packed audiences.

The band returns to Massachusetts on August 22nd. Meantime their engagements extend up to August 16th. All communications respecting the Mount Hermon Choir should be made to Messrs Shaw and Kirlew at the Refuge."

"CHILDRENS' SERVICES AT LYTHAM AND
ST ANNES ON SEA"
"Meetings were held at these two watering places from August 7th to 12th, by the five students from Mount Hermon College, Massachusetts. The week commenced with the rain and cold of which we have had so much this summer but a favourable change appeared, and most of the meetings were held in delightful sunshine. The number of workers made it possible to have services at Lytham and St Annes at the same time, and in both places, and as in the past summers, multitudes of bright faced children formed groups on the sands.

Between services, a good deal of hard work went into 'church building' on the beach, using sand and pebbles, and also 'text writing' on the sand. The Chinese lantern procession from Lytham Windmill to St Annes had been a great success, with the twinkling lanterns coming out of the darkness to the foot of the handsome statue, that tells of the grand death of those 'noble warriors of the sea' — the St Annes Lifeboat crew.

One of the most memorable meetings of the week was a gathering of people at the sea front windmill at Lytham at dusk, when the impressive singing of the quartet choir from Mount Hermon was listened to with breathless attention, and surely touched some hearts."

"THE MOUNT HERMON GOSPEL CHOIR"
"The five young men from Mr Moody's Homes and Colleges at Northfield USA, three of whom went from Manchester a few years ago — Johnnie Raynes, John Caton and George Woodhouse — returned to America in the 'City of Chicago' on Wednesday, August 22nd, carrying with them many good wishes from a large circle of friends whom they have made on both sides of the Atlantic."

AFTERWORD

During the lifetime of the great evangelist, Dwight Lyman Moody, three revival meetings took place in Manchester, an interval of nine years between each visit. His final four day mission to the city took place at the St James Hall on Oxford Street in November 1892. According to a report at that time:-

"Manchester has once more been privileged to hear the voice which has borne God's message to so many hearts, the wide world over. It was an impressive sight to see the great St James buildings filled three times daily and crowded to overflowing each night. Mr Moody spoke with his old simple downright earnestness and American quaintness, and his old knack of translating Bible stories into living narratives of every day. Those four days were soon over but it will take all eternity to finish his work.

On the last day of the Mission, Mr Moody, whose big tender heart had just been touched in its warmest corner by a visit to the Bethesda Home for Crippled Children, made one of his irrestable appeals on behalf of the Strangeways Refuges and Homes. The morning after the close of the Mission, Mr Moody visited his old friend Frank Crossley at the Star Hall in Ancoats, where he conducted his final service."

NB. Dwight L Moody died during the closing days of the nineteenth century at his home in Northfield, USA. He was buried on a hill by the name of 'Roundtop' overlooking the Connecticut River, and his beloved Northfield and Mount Hermon Schools.

THE 'TWELVE IN LATER LIFE —

ONE
John Collings Caton successfully graduated from both Princeton and Yale Universities where he obtained a BA, MA, and a BD in Theology. From the time of his first appointment as Church Minister in 1898 and up until his retirement in 1940, he remained in the service of the Church.

Frank Critchlow, Class of 1888, Mount Hermon Massachusetts.

TWO
Joseph Dooley left Mount Hermon in 1889 and began a career at the Connecticut Valley Orchard Company, New Britain, Connecticut. He returned to Manchester, England during 1900 but eventually established his roots in the United States.

THREE
Edwin Albert Cartledge was last heard of in 1902 when he made enquiries from his home in Hartford, Connecticut, regarding his long lost sister.

Alfred Beesley is seen here with his friend Stevie Collins at Mt. Hermon in APRIL 1886, a few months after his left leg was amputated.

Benjamin Platt — Class of "91" Mount Hermon.

FOUR
John Arthur Raynes on leaving Mount Hermon in 1887, was believed to have enrolled at the Boston Conservatory of Music where he could develop his natural talent. Nothing more was heard of him until 1918 when, as a Missionary, he was found to be stranded in Shangai, China.

FIVE
Alfred Beasley met with a tragic accident in December of 1885 at Northfield. It appears that a canon burst was responsible for the amputation of his left leg. After a lengthy period of confinement at Madison Hospital in New Jersey, Alfred returned to Mount Hermon to continue his schooling. His brave attempts to carry on a normal life at the school earned him outstanding recognition. The last evidence of Alfred Beasley was captured on a photograph at Northfield in 1886, aged 14 years.

Johnnie Raynes and Frank Critchlow appear in this photo of 'The Old Band' at Mount Hermon 1887.

The Mount Hermon Choir of 1888, including Frank Critchlow and John Raynes.

SIX
Fred Marchant Platt ceased his studies at Mount Hermon in April 1889 and went to live and work in Boston, Massachusetts. He became reunited with his long lost brother Benjamin in 1921, after a seventeen year absence.

SEVEN
Benjamin Marchant Platt graduated from Mount Hermon in 1891 and enrolled at the Moody Bible Institute in Chicago. In 1894 he attended Wheaton College prior to taking up studies at the Chicago Medical School where, in 1899, he received his MD. After serving two years in Honduras and a subsequent medical practice in ths US, he applied to become a Medical Missionary overseas. From 1905 to 1924, Ben Platt MD, served in the United States Foreign Missionary Society from his base in the Phillipines. His last years as a Doctor were spent in Hartford, Connecticut.

John Caton to the right Benjamin Platt to the left — as indicated in this Mount Hermon Class of 1891.

George Woodhouse (second from right — bottom row) in this 1890 Class at Mount Hermon.

Amongst this 1888/89 class at Mount Hermon are: John Caton, Fred Platt, Benjamin Platt, George Woodhouse and Josh Dooley.

John Collings Caton (seated centre bottom row)
attends his 50th NMH reunion in 1941.

EIGHT
Walter Walker has never been heard of since leaving Mount Hermon in 1890.

NINE
George Woodhouse on completion of his studies at Mount Hermon, entered Princeton University in 1891. After completing his musical course he accepted an appointment as Secretary of the Naval YMCA, in Philadelphia. As a qualified singer and pianist, he subsidised his income with concert performances at the Warner Concert Hall. In 1901 he began service at the Brooklyn Naval Young Men's Christian Association and resided in New York. It was on the 14th November 1909, whilst giving one of his stage performances that he collapsed and died. his funeral at the Brooklyn Naval YMCA was conducted by his best and lifelong friend (Rev.) John Caton. At the request of his widow, George Woodhouse's body was transported to Mount Hermon, his cherished adopted home, where he was buried amongst his favourite people and surroundings.

TEN
Frank Linley Critchlow entered Princeton University in 1892 where he remained until succcessfully graduating. After attaining an MA and BA he accepted a teaching post at Pringry School, New Jersey, a position he held before going on to the John Hopkins University where he obtained his Ph.d. From 1902 to 1934, Frank Critchlow taught at the Princeton University as a Professor of Modern Languages.

ELEVEN
George Tobin drowned in the Connecticut river on August 25th, 1884. He was buried the next day in a hillside grave at Mount Hermon.

TWELVE
Austin Charles William Morris drowned whilst attempting to rescue his friends. Eleven year old Austin was buried by the side of George Tobin and James Hill on 26th August, 1884.

The building in which the 'twelve' boys from England made their home, is still in existence, and forms a part of the modern and present day school now known as Northfield Mount Hermon (NMH). Its official title is still — 'Manchester House'.

The society known as the Manchester and Salford Boys' and Girls' Refuges, celebrated its 120th anniversary during 1989. Nowadays this very successful charity promotes the good cause under its more simplified title: 'Boys' and Girls' Welfare'.

On her return from America, the Manchester lady and some friends from the Refuges made a special visit to the grave of George Tobin's mother in Philips Park Cemetery. On the tomb she laid the flower which she had brought over from the Massachusetts burial mound.

Information and present day records regarding the 'BIG BOOK' and the 'Childrens' Own Paper' are kept by the 'Disabled Services Unit' in Manchester.

'ANGELS FROM THE MEADOW' (ODE TO AUSTIN MORRIS)

You children of the Meadow
Twixt St Michael's and St Chad's,'
Sing you Hallelujahs'
You lassies and you lads.

For down at Tommy Johnson's
Just past the Angel Steps,
There's news of little heroes
Whose courage spans great depths.

"Two little boys are drowning
In the Connecticut, U.S.A.",
When a Meadow boy espies them
And dives to save the day.

His name was Austin Morris
A courageous lad was he,
And through swift currents rushing by
Performed great bravery.

Alas, his attempts grew weaker
And having spent his strength and will,
Succumbed to his fate with the others
Till all three were silent and still.

Little Austin is now with his maker
So too is George Tobin and James Hill,
They lie side by side — in the vast open wide
At Mount Hermon — their Home on the Hill.

James Stanhope-Brown
December 1992

This aerial view taken from the CIS Building on Miller Street, Manchester shows the area known as Angel Meadow.
Photograph by kind permission of CIS.